VILLA

NO REMORSE II

by

Al McIntosh

with Dean Rinaldi

Published by Blue Mendos Publications
In association with Amazon KDP

Published in paperback 2022
Category: Memoirs & Life Story
Copyright Al McIntosh © 2022
ISBN : 9798849301006

Cover design by Jill Rinaldi © 2022

Dedication

I may be far from perfect but when I look at my four wonderful children, Sean, Chelsea, Dionne and Myles, I know that I got something in my life perfectly right.

Acknowledgements

Jill Rinaldi for the design and creation of my book covers and my good friend and ghostwriter Dean Rinaldi.

A special thank you to Maureen Flanagan, former '70s glamour model, actress, best-selling author and family friend to the Krays, for the wonderful review of the first book in the Villain No Remorse series and for endorsing my second book. Maureen works tirelessly organising Kray charitable fund-raising events for a wide range of good causes including the NHS at the Blind Beggar pub on Whitechapel Road.

Chapter 1

Glasgow City Central Train Station 1976.

With an envelope containing the one thousand pounds that he had just taken from his safety deposit box tucked firmly in his inside jacket pocket along with a new toothbrush, Al raced along platform one and boarded the Glasgow to Euston London train. He peered out of the window briefly before closing it and sitting back in his seat.

"I don't fucking believe this," Al thought as he shook his head vigorously. *"We had it made, everything was sweet and now…. it's all gone in an instant!"*

The train guard passed by Al's window blowing his whistle. The train shunted several times and then slowly edged out of the train station on its six hour, three hundred and forty-three mile journey to Euston, London.

"We could have all made good money. I spelt it out to Kurt and told him that we could have worked with Joey Flemming. We did the leading on Mondays and they could have had Tuesdays and so on, so me and the Balgrayhill Boys could have both rinsed out some good money while it was there for the taking," Al thought as he pushed himself back into the seat. *"But oh no, that fucking lunatic, Joey Flemming, just had to play the big hard man."*

Al sighed and turned to face the window as the train gathered pace.

"Seven, eight hundred and some weeks over a thousand pounds, and now it's all down the pisser because of his giant ego," Al thought. *"I just don't get people like that. It's just violence for the sake of violence. It's as if having some kind of hard man reputation is more important than having a pocketful of money, being out*

having a few drinks with your mates and chatting up a couple of pretty girls."

A wry smile crept across his face.

"I made you pay though, Joey Flemming," Al thought as his smile became broader. "Running around town telling everyone what you're going to do me. Well, you needed a lesson and that is what you got when I introduced a twelve-inch piece of metal pipe to your ugly mug."

Al let out a short chuckle.

"It was a nice touch having just given him a severe beating, to rest the pipe on his head and issue a warning 'If I ever have to come for you again, I'll fucking kill you," Al remembered saying.

The smile left his face.

"I didn't think for one minute that he'd come back for me with a double barrel shotgun," Al thought as he moved around to get more comfortable. "Nicking that mannequin saved my life. He came to take me out. Thank fuck I saw those barrels come through the letter box."

Al looked up as a ticket inspector passed his seat.

"I hate walking away from good money," Al thought as reached into his pocket for a Mars bar that he'd bought at the confectionary kiosk. "We had the police taking a hundred pounds a day to just let us do what the fuck we wanted. They were even letting us know when a raid was coming. It was sweet. If only Kurt could have convinced Joey Flemming to get on board with making a few quid."

Al tore the top of the chocolate bar's wrapper, peeled it back and took a bite.

"I just don't get what it was that I did to give Officer Dibble such a hard on for me," Al thought before taking a second bite from the delicious chocolate bar. *"Even the police I had on side couldn't get their heads around it."*

Al paused for moment.

"I can only think of once when Dibble and a younger officer followed me into a house all set for demolition that I was checking out for lead. He called out 'Jack Wilson' like he knew me. When he asked what I was doing in the house I apologised and told them that I was embarrassed and was caught short and needed to take a pee. But he wasn't having none of it and went on to tell me how my name kept on coming up and yet there was nothing on me, no previous arrests or convictions," Al thought as he popped the last of the chocolate bar into his mouth, scrunched up the wrapper and put it back into his pocket. *"I told him that I was clean, but he wasn't having any of it. Reckoned I was in there checking out lead. The only thing I can think he took exception to, was when I asked why the leading bothered him so much and asked if he wanted it for himself."*

Al chewed the chocolate and caramel bar and then swallowed.

"I'll never get bored with the taste of a Mars Bar," Al thought. *"There was no need for that kicking him and his pals did down at the station. Big and brave in their uniforms and in truth they don't give a toss whether you're innocent or not. To top it all they nicked me for assaulting them and it was me that was getting the shit kicked out of him."*

Al released a bright, sardonic, smile.

"Old Dibble didn't count on coming face to face with my Mammy," Al thought as the train passed through a station. *"When you came staggering out of that pub, Dibble, I bet you didn't expect to have to fend off an old woman battering the fuck out of you with her metal horseshoe."*

Al sniggered as he visualised Officer Dibble getting battered to the ground by his Mammy.

"Big brave Dibble having to tell his mates that he was set about by six tooled up thugs," Al thought as he turned back to face the empty seat opposite him.

Al could hear the faint sounds of *'Can't Get By Without You'* by The Real Thing. Then he heard the Radio One DJ, Tom Browne, who hosted the Sunday Top twenty chart hits, begin to introduce the next record when it was cut off and *'Howzat'* by Sherbet began to play.

"It must a kid further down the carriage that's been tape recording the top twenty," Al thought.

As the distant sound of *'Dancing Queen'* by Abba played, Al found himself thinking about Brian, his younger brother.

"Brian will be alright. He knows the rules. When it comes on top you've just got to get yourself out," Al thought. *"I can't help thinking about Wullie."*

Al closed his eyes momentarily before glancing up towards the train's smoke-stained ceiling.

"I hope he gets off back to his gamekeeping job in Aberdeenshire," Al thought. *"There's something not quite right with my brother Wullie. I can still see him now, leaning up against the wall outside the Vulcan pub, all dressed up for my twenty first birthday bash, and as calm as you like he announces that he's going to kill Mammy one of these days."*

Al looked down at his hands. He stretched out his fingers before curling them back into fists.

"Mammy and Da, they both have a lot to answer for," Al thought. *"A vicious, brutal, psychotic excuse of a Maw and an abhorrent drunk who cares for nothing but his Four Crown wine."*

Al could just about make out the top ten countdown when *'Mississippi'* by Pussycat began to play.

"Who the hell would go out and buy a record like that?" Al thought.

The song finally finished, and Al was left with just the sound of the train's wheels on the track.

"I've got a warrant out for my arrest in London and now another in Glasgow," Al thought as his heart sank. *"I'm going to have to keep my head down and stay out of trouble."*

***

Finally, the train rolled into Euston train station. He jumped to his feet, took a deep breath, and then walked down the platform towards the exit. He handed his ticket to the inspector while continuing his pace. Al stopped briefly as he stepped outside the station and looked around at the bustling traffic and people of every race, colour and creed moving back and forth in a perpetual state of necessity. He spotted a red telephone box and bolted towards it. Once inside he lifted the receiver and began to dial. The phone rang several times and just as Al was about to hang up, he heard a voice, so he pushed the coin into the slot.

Voice: Hello, who is this?

Al: Is that any way to greet an old friend, you miserable sod?

Voice: Who is this?

Al: Its Al, Al McIntosh.

Voice: Well, fuck my old boots, Al. I thought you were dead. Well, gone back North and that's as good as dead as far as I'm concerned.

Al: It's good to hear your voice, Toby.

Toby: Yours too mate. So, what, are you back in London on a visit or what?

Al: I need your help, Toby.

Toby: Of course, mate. What do you need, a bird, a few quid, what?

Al began to laugh.

Al: A tasty little sort would be nice but that's not top of my list right now. I'm alright for money but what I do need is a place to stay for a while.

Toby: No problem, Al. Can you get yourself over to Lewisham?

Al: Yeah, no problem.

Al turned towards a line of bus stops outside the station.

Toby: Can you remember where I am?

Al: Yeah, I remember there being three tower blocks just off the High Street.

Toby: That's right, you've got it. Kemsley, Bredgar and Malling Block. I'm in Bredgar.

Toby gave Al his full address.

Al: I appreciate this, Toby.

Toby: No problem, it's what mates do, Al. So get yourself over here. I can feel a session coming on.

Al: You don't change.

Toby: That's a good thing, right?

Al: Yeah, I suppose so. I'll see you shortly.

Toby: Yeah, be lucky.

Al stepped out of the telephone box and took a deep breath of London air.

"I fucking love this place!" Al thought.

"Excuse me, pal," Al called out to a uniformed staff member of British Rail.

"Yes, mate," was the reply along with a broad smile.

"I need to get to Lewisham," Al said, shrugging his shoulders.

"Bus or train?"

"Bus will be fine," Al said.

"Right, see that bus over there?" the guy from British rail pointed to a lone red bus stationary at the bus stop. "You take that bus to Elephant and Castle and then right outside the pub on the corner you'll see a bus stop. You need to take the '136' bus to Lewisham Centre. It should take you a little over an hour depending on the traffic."

"Thank you," Al said as he peered towards the stationary bus. "I appreciate your help."

"No problem, enjoy your time in London."

Al could feel his body recharging with every step he took in the capital. Al paid the bus driver, went upstairs and sat at the back of the bus by the window. He found a newspaper on the seat. He read that James Hunt had won the Formula 1 World Championship in his works-built McLaren M23 against the reigning champion and his main rival, Niki Lauda.

"I'm not really a fan of Formula 1," Al thought as he read through the newspaper article. *"But you've got to admire James Hunt. The man just wasn't born with a filter between his brain and mouth."*

Al thought back to an interview he'd caught on television where Stirling Moss was interviewing James Hunt and talked about changes to the regulations and said, "Yet you're still so fast. How do you do it?" Hunt remained completely expressionless and answered, "Big balls." Al remembering chuckling before turning the TV off and going to meet his friends at The Vulcan pub.

"I can still see him standing on the track in Long Beach shaking his fist at the driver that put him to the wall and then gave him a right dressing down about his lack of driving skills while being interviewed on television," Al thought as he closed the newspaper and put it back on the seat next to him.

"If there was ever an anti-establishment icon in the world of sport, it's James Hunt," Al thought as he remembered an article showing Hunt with a patch stitched onto his overalls reading: SEX: Breakfast of Champions!

The hour passed quickly and Al got off the bus in Lewisham High Street. He looked up at the three eighteen-storey tower blocks housing a total of two hundred and four dwellings. Al looked from left to right and then hurried across the road and walked quickly towards the three apartment blocks. From the corner of his eye, he spotted a mixed group of six chatting enthusiastically outside a telephone box. Al found that he had to take a second look. He had never seen anything quite like it. The three girls had a combination of either shaven or extremely short hair with a brightly coloured Mohican style haircut. Their eyes had heavy black make-up and one girl had what looked like a safety pin clamped into her mouth and cheek. The taller girl with bright electric blue colouring in her hair had several earrings in her ear joined together by a chain. She wore a black T-shirt with 'Punk' written across it in red lettering and a short tartan skirt with tights that had holes in them. Another of the girls wore a similar T-shirt in white with 'Damned' written in gothic style black lettering. The three lads wore what Al thought were studded leather dog collars and leather jackets covered in silver studs and badges. Their hair had been greased to stand up.

"Sure you don't want to take a photograph?" the taller of the girls called out.

"Live and let live is my view," Al replied with a smile.

As Al approached Bredgar Block he caught sight of his friend, Toby Anderson, running a wet rag over a Mercedes 450SL finished in a beautiful brown with matching colour wheel covers.

"Is that you, Toby?" Al called out as he approached his friend.

"Why, Al, you old reprobate," Toby said as he dropped the rag, wiped his hand on his blue Levi jeans, and then walked towards Al with his hand outstretched. "It's good to see you mate."

Toby was slim and stood at a little over five foot ten inches tall. His mousey brown hair was styled in a middle parting and covered his ears.

"What's all this then?" Al said, pointing towards the car.

"It'll be gone by the morning," Toby said, looking down at his watch. "How do you fancy a drink?"

"I could murder a drink," Al said.

"Good, me too," Toby said, looking down at Al's hands. "You've not got a bag?"

Al shook his head.

"I take it you had to leave in a hurry," Toby said with a chuckle.

"Something like that," Al said.

Al followed Toby back towards the Mercedes. He looked in at the tan leather interior.

"Very nice," Al said.

Toby started the engine and slipped the automatic gear shifter into Drive. He checked his rear-view mirror and slowly began to move away.

"Is the pub far?" Al said.

"Nah, just up on the Lee High Road," Toby said as he reached down and turned the radio cassette player on. *'You'll Never Find Another Love Like Mine'* by Lou Rawls pounded through the speakers. Al winced and covered his ears.

"Sorry about that," Toby said, as he quickly reached out and turned down the volume.

Toby put the indicator on and then came to a halt outside the 'Sultan' pub. He spotted a couple of young kiddies eating a packet of crisps on chairs outside the pub. Toby was out of the car and leading the way to the pub.

"I'm getting a right thirst on," Toby said with a wink.

Al smiled and followed him into the pub. As they walked towards the bar, Al looked around at the dark wooden panelling and the glass wall lights between the stained-glass windows. There was a dart board, pool table and jukebox, with two young black girls wearing heels and short pleated skirts reading the disc menu. One looked over and smiled before turning back abruptly when *'More, More, More'* by Andrea True Connection began to play.

"Buster, how are you mate?" Toby said as he shook hands with the man behind the bar.

"That bloke must have a fifty-inch chest!" Al thought.

"Can't complain," Buster answered in a low, gruff voice.

"This is a mate, and I mean a good mate of mine, and he'll be using your pub for a while," Toby said, standing to one side so Buster could see Al.

"Nice to meet you, Buster. I'm Al."

Buster half smiled and nodded.

"What are you boys having?" Buster said as he reached for a pint jug.

"I'm going to give the bitter a miss and try some of that Carling Black Label in a straight glass, please Buster," Toby said before peering around the pub and waving towards two men sitting at a table by the slot machine. "Can you put a couple behind the bar for Donny and Trevor?"

Buster nodded as he put the pint jug away and grabbed a straight glass from under the bar.

"I'll have a whiskey," Al said.

"Anything with it?" Buster said as he slowly filled the glass with golden liquid.

"Just ice, and can you make it a double?" Al said.

Buster placed the pint of lager on the bar and reached for a bottle of Bells whiskey. Toby picked up the lager glass and took a small sip before putting it back on the bar.

"Do you know what... that ain't bad," Toby said before reaching over and taking a longer sip. "Not bad at all!"

"I'll tell you something, after this long hot summer, the sales of lager have gone through the roof," Buster said. "I'm bringing in Harp and Heineken lagers, Toby. The punters can't get enough of it and I'm having birds drinking half pints of lager with a lemonade top.

"The summer of 1976 will go down in history," Toby said with a broad grin.

"It was hot, but I was too busy leading and making serious money to notice," Al thought as he took a sip of his whiskey.

The door of the pub swung open and one of the little boys that was outside chomping on a packet of crisps outside peered in.

"Dad, can we have some lemonade, please?" the little boy called out.

Buster waved over to one of the pub's many customers and held up a bottle of R Whites lemonade.

"Let's grab a seat," Toby said.

"So is this a local for you?" Al said as he glanced around the pub.

"Well kind of," Toby said as he nodded towards a young couple as they entered the pub. "I come in here because the people around here use the pub like a home from a home. They're a good bunch and there's rarely any trouble."

"I suppose Buster would take care of any trouble," Al said.

Toby chuckled.

"He's a big, intimidating fella alright but it's his other half, Lorraine, that calls the shots and she's not to be messed with," Toby said. "This is a place of business and doing deals, you know the kind of stuff that gets moved on like jewellery, records and cigarettes, and it's pretty social in here too.

"You're still looking pretty affluent, Toby, is business good?" Al said before briefly turning towards the two girls standing by the jukebox.

'This Is It' by Melba Moore had the two girls dancing and slowly gyrating their hips in time to the music.

"I'm still into moving motors," Toby said as he removed his brown leather bomber style jacket and put it over the back of the chair. "Only I'm not really selling them to your average punters anymore."

Al took a sip from his drink and leaned forward.

"Between you and me mate, I'm into ringing motors," Toby said softly. "But not on my own doorstep."

"What, you nick them and sell them on at auctions or with mates in other parts of London?" Al said.

"No," Toby said, slowly shaking his head. "I've gone all international, mate. When I'm not here I'm drinking at the Ram, the Pitts Head in Woolwich or the Royal Oak in Canning Town. I met a

Bubble a year or so back and it turns out that he's got an upmarket car front in Cyprus."

"A Bubble, Cyprus?" Al said, nearly choking on his drink.

"Yeah, Cyprus the Greek Island and Bubble as in Bubble and Squeak… Greek," Toby said with a chuckle. "If you Northerners want to live down here, you'll have to learn the lingo."

"What do you mean, like Toby Jug…. Mug?" Al said before bursting out laughing.

"Fuck you," Toby said with a broad smile. "I had enough of that at school."

"So how does that bit of business work then?" Al said.

"I have a fella on the firm at Heathrow Airport. He works in the car park. It's easy, Al. My mate, the Bubble, tells me what he wants and when a Mercedes or a Porsche gets left for any length of time in the car park, I get a phone call and that's it. I go over in some cheap and nasty motor that I've nicked that day, buy a short-term parking ticket and then have the high-end motor away. The chances are, by the time the owners get back, the motor would have been shipped off down to Cyprus and be sitting on the Bubble's forecourt."

"Nice one," Al said, raising his glass.

"I must have shipped him a good sixty or seventy motors in the last year and my shopping list is two pages long," Toby continued quietly. "The thing is, they drive on the right-hand side of the road in Cyprus, and they love a high-end motor. Bubble seems to have the old bill on the island straightened out, so it's all sweet."

"I'm pleased for you Toby, you were always one of the good guys," Al said.

"Cheers," Toby said as he raised his hand to Buster and motioned him to bring over two of the same.

"I wish I had started on this lager earlier," Toby said before drinking the last drops in the glass.

"Anyway, how have you been and more to the point why are you back?" Toby said and then let out a small belch. "Haven't you got a warrant out for your arrest down here?"

"Yeah," Al said before letting out a sigh. "I've got one out for me in Glasgow too."

"Fuck me, that's not good," Toby said as the barmaid put the drink on the table. "Cheers sweetheart."

"You're telling me," Al said.

"So, what's the plan?"

"I don't have one right now," Al said. "I just need a place to get my head down and then take some time to sort myself out."

"Well I'm happy to help mate," said Toby. "In fact, your timing is perfect because I've been seeing this cracking little sort in Camden, sweet little thing, you know, marriage material and all that."

"Good for you," Al said.

"That's not to say you can pass something up when it falls on your lap, face or anything else," Toby said as the two friends chinked glass. "Well, this bird has been going on at me about moving in with her and I've been prevaricating, you know, putting it off until it all lines up right in my head and this morning over a coffee I thought 'fuck it' why not and then a couple of hours later you phoned saying that you need a place."

"What, you're letting me have your place?" Al said.

"Yes mate. It's got two bedrooms, dry, warm, costs fuck all to run and the rent is right up to date," Toby said. "All I ask is that you keep paying the rent on time and any other bills just in case it all goes shit shaped at some point with this bird in Camden."

"No problem," Al said. "It will be done."

"How are you for dosh?" Toby whispered. "Are you alright for a few quid?"

"Yeah, I'm sorted for now," Al said.

"Look, I can use you to drive a few motors about if you like," Toby said. "The money's good."

"No, but cheers, Toby," Al said, nodding gratefully. "I need to keep my head down and stay out of trouble's way."

"Mate I understand and respect that. However, if you find yourself needing a bit of work then it's always there, plus I've got another little side line going."

Al looked at him with a quizzical expression.

"Because the motors that Bubble wants don't always come in as and when I need them, I've rented a little lock up and have a couple of lads stripping down high-end motors for spares, and then what's left I have shipped off to be crushed. We've only done a half dozen motors and it's turning in a fair few quid," Toby said.

"I'll keep that in mind," Al said. "Cheers mate."

***

Al and Toby arrived back at the flat in Bredgar block just after 2.00am. At just gone 11.00, Buster had pulled the curtains around the pub and locked the place down with scores of locals still sipping on pints, playing pool or throwing darts.

"I think some dirty bastard has pissed in the lift," Al said as he stepped inside.

"That might have been me last night," Toby said, laughing raucously.

"You dirty bastard," Al said as he leaned against the side of the lift.

21

"I'm just having a bubble with you," Toby said as he pressed the floor select button.

"What you're having a bubble and squeak, Greek with me?" Al slurred as he shifted his feet when the lift began to climb.

"Nah, having a bubble is having a laugh," Toby said as the elevator came to a halt and the doors opened.

"You cockneys confuse the fuck out of me with all this 'dog and bone' phone and 'pork pies' lies stuff," Al said as he followed Toby out into the hallway and down towards the flat's front door at the far end.

"I ain't no cockney," Toby said with a slur. "I'm a South Londoner born and bred on the right side of the river."

"It's all bollocks to me," Al said as he followed Toby into the flat, down the hallway and into the front room.

"Yeah, you're right, it is." Toby said as he turned on the light switch.

"Fuck me what a shit hole," Al thought as he took a quick glimpse around the room. *"There's dirty dinner plates, a half full cup of coffee and a fish and chip soiled newspaper wrapping on the settee."*

"You can crash in the back bedroom. The bed's made up," Toby said. "Well, there's bedding on it anyway. It's good to have you back in London mate, and I'm pleased that you came to me."

"I appreciate what you're doing for me," Al said as he moved the fish and chip papers and sat down on the settee.

"I've learned some stuff and you need to know, Al, that some people will just love you, mate, while others will love being around you, but most will love you for what you can do for them. The key is understanding the difference mate. And on that deep and meaningful note I'm off to bed," Toby said before letting out a long, thunderous, burp.

Chapter 2

l was awake, shaved and showered just after 7.00am.

"These clothes could do with a clean, but I've got fuck all else to wear," Al thought as he raised his shirt and sniffed the arm pits.

After putting the kettle on in the kitchen, Al washed out a dirty cup and made himself a black coffee as he didn't trust the milk in Toby's fridge. He traipsed back through to the front room and slouched back on the settee.

"Right, I've got to start making some plans," Al thought as he blew into the boiling hot coffee. *"I've got just over a thousand pounds but that won't last forever."*

Al took a small sip and then looked around the living room.

"This place is in a right state, and I can't be looking at this," Al thought.

Having put the hot drink on the coffee table, Al set about collecting up all the cutlery, plates, and cups from around the room and took them into the kitchen. He found a single black plastic rubbish bag in one of the drawers and proceeded to throw away everything he perceived to be rubbish.

"How can a person live like this?" Al thought. *"I have to give it to Toby, he always dresses like he's minted, but this place looks like a bomb has gone off."*

It was just after 9.30am when Toby finally rolled out of bed.

"Morning Al," Toby said as he stood at the doorway to the lounge. "What the fuck's happened here? What, did you shit the bed or something?"

"I had to tidy up mate," Al said as leaned back on the settee. "I don't know how you can live with all that shit around you."

"I don't have time for all that tidying up bollocks," Toby said. "I'm busy with earning a few quid, drinking with my mates and chasing skirt."

"What, you bring birds back here when it looks like a doss hole?" Al said.

"Oi, less of the slagging my place off," Toby said with a chuckle. "I was thinking about getting some little tart in to clean the place and maybe do a bit of washing, cooking some grub and that."

"So why didn't you?" Al said as he sipped at his freshly made coffee.

"I met Janine, the bird in Camden, and I pretty much stayed at hers most weekends. Anyway, it's yours now so you can do what you like," Toby said as he turned away and walked down the hallway towards the kitchen.

"The kettle has just boiled," Al called out after him.

"What's your plans today?" Toby called back, spooning a heap of coffee into a mug.

"I'm going to need some clothes," Al called back. "I left in a bit of a hurry."

Toby entered the room carrying a hot cup of coffee and then sat down in the armchair by the television.

"I can give Shirley a ring and ask her to get you some bits and pieces," Toby said as he lifted the telephone receiver.

"Who's Shirley?" Al said.

"She lives in the next block. I've known her since my school days mate. Shirley runs a small team of shoplifters and is happy to take orders," Toby said as he began dialling "Everything is half retail price. What do you want?"

"Er... trousers, shirts, socks, pants, shoes and a leather jacket. It can be black or brown, I don't care," Al said.

Toby took Al's clothes sizes and passed the details on to Shirley.

"There you go, all sorted Al," Toby said as he put the telephone receiver down. "She reckons she'll have your clobber today, so I said we'll meet her at the Sultan later."

"Cheers, Toby," Al said.

"Mate, why pay full retail prices when you can get what you want at half price?" Toby said. "I ain't kidding when I say that just about everything in my wardrobe has come from Shirley, and I'm talking suits, jackets, shirts, you know, the whole nine yards of good quality gear. In the meantime, take a wander down to my wardrobe and pick yourself out some gear to wear. There's plenty to choose from."

Al was up and sorting through Toby's wardrobe. He settled on a brown pair of flared trousers with a three-button high waistband and a cream shirt with a butterfly collar and brown leather shoes. As he checked out his reflection in the full-length wall mirror, he heard *(Shake Shake Shake) Shake Your Booty'* by KC & The Sunshine Band being played. He took one last look at himself and then strutted up the hallway to the living room.

Toby was standing over the stereo system reading a K-Tel Hits Album cover. He turned towards Al and began singing.

"Shake shake shake, shake shake shake, shake your booty, shake your booty."

"Smart, very smart," Toby said with a huge cheeky grin. "You'll be knocking those birds down at the Sultan, bandy."

"Right, Al," Toby said as he rubbed his hands together. "I've got to see a man about a dog. It's just a quick bit of business so I'll see you at the Sultan, what, about one o'clock?"

"Yeah, sure," Al said.

"Here you go mate," Toby said, handing Al a set of front door keys. "Just come and go as you like, alright. It's as good as your place now."

"I might go and find a café and get some breakfast," Al said. "Any suggestions?"

"There is a place on the High Street but the fry up ain't up to much and the geezer who owns the place is a miserable git," Toby said as he put his brown leather jacket on. "I'll be passing a place on the Old Kent Road, Peckham. Joe's Café and it's a proper greasy spoon, you know. They do a proper fry up, with bangers, bacon, fried bread the lot, if you fancy it."

Al beamed and grabbed his jacket.

Joe's Café served up a huge breakfast which Al had struggled to finish. While sitting back he could hear car dealers around him talking about auctions, difficult motors to shift and places that would do deals. Al smiled to himself.

"London is always buzzing with something going on somewhere," Al thought as he put his knife and fork together on the plate and left the café.

Having checked his watch, Al decided to walk back along the Old Kent Road towards Lewisham. He wanted time to clear his head and make plans for the future.

It was just after 1.00pm when Al arrived at the Sultan pub on Lee High Road.

"Alright, Al," Buster said as he approached the bar. "Whiskey, is it?"

"Yeah, cheers Buster, make it a double," Al said, scanning the bar.

The group he had seen the day before with the coloured hair, dog collars and studded leather jackets were sitting together in the far corner chatting.

"I've not seen that kind of fashion before," Al muttered.

"I think they call themselves Punk Rockers," Buster said as he handed Al his drink. "They're harmless enough."

"Oh, right," Al said as he reached for his drink and sat down at the same table that he and Toby had been at the night before.

When *'Who Loves You'* by The Four Seasons played, Al glanced over to the jukebox and saw the same two girls he'd seen the day before, scanning through the record menu.

One of the girls turned briefly and smiled. She had long coral-black hair that swooped over her shoulders and curtained her oval face. The brief stare from her vivacious brown eyes was intense. Al could feel his heart beginning to pound against his chest as she slowly made her way across the bar towards him.

"Do I know you?" the girl said with a seductive smile.

"Er, no I don't think so, I'm Al."

"It's just that I saw you looking at me, or maybe it was my friend that captured your attention," the girl said, maintaining direct eye contact.

"I just like the record," Al said before taking a sip of his drink.

"Well, and there was me thinking that you were looking at me. I'm Shanice and my friend," the girl said while turning and waving to her friend by the juke box, "Is Imani."

"Nice to meet you, Shanice," Al said. "Can I buy you a drink?"

"It's a bit too early for me, but a game of pool would be nice," Shanice said with a smile that revealed her dazzling white teeth. "You do play pool, don't you, Al?"

"Sure, I'm game," Al said as he stood up and motioned Buster to pour him another drink.

Al followed Shanice down the bar to the pool table. He couldn't help but notice how her short slinky powder pink satin dress was nipped at the waist and gathered to accentuate her hip movement.

"Do you mind?" Shanice said as she reached across the pool table for the triangle shaped rack.

"No, please do," Al said as he sorted through the cues for the best two.

Shanice took the rack in both hands and slid it across the green felt before placing the yellow 'one' spot ball at the apex of the rack.

"She's done this more than once or twice," Al thought.

Shanice placed the 'nine' striped ball to the left and the blue 'two' to the right before placing the 'eight' black ball in the centre of the third row. She then picked up a 'five' spot ball and positioned it in the left corner and a 'twelve' stripe in the right far corner. Then she quickly placed the other balls randomly in the remaining spaces.

Al couldn't help but notice how Shanice's dress rode up as she leaned forward to slide the rack over the table's white spot.

Shanice checked to see that the balls were tightly packed before removing the rack. Al held out the two best pool cues so that Shanice could make her choice. With her ebony eyes firmly fixed on Al's, she reached over and took the cue in his right hand while allowing her fingers to lightly brush against his.

Al could feel himself becoming aroused.

"Shall I break?" Shanice said as she lined up the white ball.

"Go for it," Al said as he stepped back from the table.

"Would you like to make this game interesting?" Shanice asked.

"What do you have in mind?" Al said.

Shanice stood up and placed her pool cue on the corner of the table and walked suggestively back towards Al. She stopped directly in front of him, ran her hands over her curves, and then bent forward to whisper into his ear.

"Let's say five pounds if I win, and if you win," Shanice whispered seductively, "I'll suck you off."

Al could feel his mouth go dry while his manhood pressed firmly against his trousers.

"Okay," Al said hoarsely.

He cleared his throat and then took a five-pound note from his wallet and put it on the side of the table.

Shanice took her cue and then positioned the white ball slightly off centre. She leaned down, lined up her cue and powered through a shot that sent the second balls hurtling towards the side pockets. The blue spot crashed into the back of the pocket and sunk. The 'five' spot pounded off the back cushion, hit the corner and rocketed up the table where it rebounded from the end before hurtling back down the table and landing in the far right pocket.

"This bird is a pro," Al thought as he watched Shanice scatter the balls around the table before landing squarely in the pockets.

Slowly but surely the arousal died as he realised that he'd been conned by a pro.

Shanice walked around the table to find the best strategy to dislodge her final ball, the black, which was hidden behind the 'twelve' stripe. Shanice finally settled with her focus narrowed down the cue. She sent the white ball streaking across the table. It bounced off the far corner and scurried back, catching the corner of the black ball which immediately began to spin before careering off to the left and dropping down into the pocket.

Shanice looked up at Al with a victorious grin.

"I believe that's my five-pound note," Shanice said as she plucked it from the table.

"Well played," Al said, slowly clapping his hands. "Very well played, and in every sense of the word."

"Fancy double or nothing?" Shanice asked as she tilted her head towards her friend Imani by the Jukebox.

"Maybe another time," Al said, as he spotted Toby standing by the bar. "I've got a bit of business to do."

"It was nice playing with you," Shanice said before pouting her plump heart-shaped lips and blowing him a kiss.

"I see you met Shanice and Imani," Toby said with a snigger.

"It was the best five pounds I've ever spent. That girl can play, really play," Al said before finishing his drink.

"Yeah, right," Toby said with a raucous laugh. "We both know what you were hoping for."

"Well, I can't say the thought didn't cross my mind," Al said as he held up his empty glass.

"That's her party trick," Toby said as he raised his lager glass. "I have seen scores of geezers part with money in the hope of having their old todger sorted by Shanice. Did she offer you the double with Imani?"

Al nodded.

"Yeah, mate, even I had to have a pop at that, and my pool is shit," Toby said. "No one, to my knowledge, has ever beaten Shanice. Al,

I've asked her out and even propositioned her once with fifty quid and she blanked me, mate."

"Nice little scam she has going," Al thought.

'The Tears of a Clown' by Smokey Robinson & The Miracles had just started playing when a middle-aged woman with long, lavish, moon-gleam gold hair plonked two large plastic bags at Al's feet. Al looked up to see her lambent jade-green eyes looking down on him.

"You must be Al," the woman said as she pulled out a chair and sat down. "I'm Shirley and mine's a Port and lemon."

"Buster," Toby called. "Can we have another round here and a Port and lemon for Shirley, please? Cheers."

"So where having you been hiding this tasty young morsel?" Shirley said as she looked Al up and down while running her tongue slowly over her succulent puffy pink lips. "He looks delicious."

"Give it a rest," Toby said as he handed her the Port and lemon.

Shirley closed her eyes and took a long sip of her drink.

"Don't you just love that first drink of the day because you just know there will be more to come?" Shirley said as she put the glass down. "Okay, Al, I've got you four pairs of trousers, seven shirts, seven pairs of underpants, socks and a black leather bomber Jacket. I've left all the prices on, and it comes to sixty-one pounds, but we'll call it thirty quid, okay?"

Al nodded eagerly and reached into his trouser pocket.

"My only concern would be that the underpants are not quite big enough," Shirley said with an alluring smile.

"So, tell me handsome," Shirley said as she lit a cigarette. "What brings you to this part of London?"

"Al's moved here," Toby said before Al could answer. "He'll be taking over my old flat for a while."

"Nice," Shirley said as she eyed Al up and down.

"You will have to forgive her mate, Shirley is the world's biggest flirt," Toby said with a chuckle. "But if push came to shove and a bloke was to make a move, she'd run a mile."

"Hey you, stop giving away all my secrets," Shirley said before stubbing the cigarette out in the glass ashtray.

"There you go," Al said as he handed Shirley six five-pound notes. "Thanks."

"Right, before Toby buggers off chasing some bit of skirt, you make sure that he gives you my telephone number. My girls and I can get just about anything if it's in a shop and it'll be half price," Shirley said as she rose from the table. "Right, I've got people to see and places to go."

Al watched as she strutted through the pub towards the ladies' restroom.

"She's a bit of a card," Toby said. "I used to baby sit for her when I was at school and even back then she would be a right flirt, just enough to hold your interest, although it was also clear that she wasn't actually available."

"I have a lot of respect for shoplifters," Al said as he pushed the dirty ashtray away. "There would be kids on council estates all over wearing hand-me-downs for school if it wasn't for the heavily discounted gear from shoplifters."

Toby nodded.

"All my school clobber came from Shirley, as did just about everyone's on the estate," Toby said.

***

Toby moved out of the flat the following day to move in with his girlfriend, Janine, in Camden. Al bought a second-hand Hoover, bedding and a full bag of house cleaning goods. Within a few days it became a home that Al was comfortable to spend time in. Toby had taken all his records except the 'Juke Box Jive 40 All Time Rock 'n' Roll Greats' double album with the image of an American style juke box on the cover. The days passed slowly with Al intent on remaining under the radar. The Sultan became his local and he quickly made friends, and although he tried on two further occasions to beat Shanice at pool... He failed.

Chapter 3

Al was nursing a bit of a hangover after a heavy session at the Sultan pub the night before. It was well past 3.00am when he arrived back at the flat. He sat on the settee and emptied out his envelope onto the coffee table. He rifled through his 'get away' money, put all the notes together by their denomination and then counted them out on the coffee table.

"Fuck me I've gone through a bloody fortune," Al thought as he held up the remaining notes. *"I've got just over a hundred and forty pounds left. I'm going to have to get a bit of work. Maybe I'll do a couple of smash and grabs. Any jewellery will sell quickly at the Sultan. At least that will give me a bit of walking around money for a while."*

Al took a sip of his coffee.

"I don't fancy staying in and I can't spend another day at the Sultan drinking all day. I'll take a trip into the West End," Al thought as put his new coffee mug back on the table. *"It's my sister Doreen's birthday soon. I know, I'll have a mooch around the sights, check out a few shops and get her something nice to send back."*

Al drank the last of his coffee, took the mug out into the kitchen and washed it. He wandered back into the bedroom and sat on the corner of his freshly made bed to slip his shoes on. He took one last look in the mirror to comb his hair and left the flat. He took a red bus up into the West End where he listened to a group of Jamaican lads talking about the Notting Hill Carnival back in the summer and how it all kicked off with the old bill battering party goers indiscriminately with their wooden truncheons.

Al got on a second bus and got off on the Kings Road in Chelsea. He wandered up and down the main road, stopping briefly outside a shop at number 430 named 'SEX'. It was owned by Vivienne

Westwood and Malcolm McLaren. He peered inside to see clothes that looked very similar to the punk rockers he saw when he first arrived in Lewisham. Al continued up the Kings Road and then stopped outside the 'Man in the Moon' pub. Outside by the entrance, was a handwritten sign advertising a range of sandwiches. Al stepped in and ordered a pint of Carlsberg lager and a cheese salad sandwich. He sat by the window and watched Londoners racing around from shop to shop. Once he had finished, Al left the pub and followed the main road up to Regent Street in Piccadilly Circus. The road was packed with taxis, red buses and heavily laden pedestrians with shopping bags crossing sporadically. As he passed by the Eros Cinema, he looked up to see that 'Clockwork Nympho' was the feature movie.

"That takes me back to those days in Soho," Al thought as he marched on. "My good friends Mae West, Jean Harlow, Harry the Poof and me running all those blue movies and girlie books for Bernie Silverman. I wonder what happened to Gas Man, Eddy and Louis the fence.

Al's heart sank a little as an image of the young, green eyed, Irish girl, Jo, came to mind.

"I never did get a chance to say goodbye. I wonder if she's still even in London or has gone back to Ireland. I hope that everything worked out for her," Al thought as he made way down the bustling pavements.

The traffic congestion was continuous with horns hooting and the occasional scream up as a taxi driver cut up another driver. Al peered up at the Piccadilly Theatre and saw 'Very Good Eddie' in huge red lettering, and 'Absolutely First Class Musical' in smaller red lettering underneath. He continued to walk on past the gargantuan 'Enjoy Coca-Cola' billboard before peering briefly at the tourists sitting on the steps underneath the 'Eros' statue. Al increased his pace until he entered Oxford Street. It was there that he spotted a colossal white sign with an EMI logo on the left and

His Masters Voice in the middle and an image of the HMV logo all in red.

"I know," Al thought as gazed through the window. "I'll get Doreen an album. She likes music."

Al entered the shop and gawped at the row upon row of vinyl record genres. He passed by the Classical, Jazz, Country & Western and Blues and stopped by the Current Charts section.

"Now, what would Doreen like?" Al thought as he thumbed through the bright, colourful album covers.

Finally his eyes rested on *'Arrival'* by Abba in the new release section.

"That's it," Al thought as he reached out and picked up the album cover featuring Benny (Smudge) Anderson, Björn Ulvaeus, Agnetha Fältskog and Anni-Frid Lyngstad sitting inside a glass fronted helicopter and the lettering 'ABBA' in mirror writing and 'Arrival'.

He turned the cover over and began to read what tracks were featured. When he read *'Dancing Queen'*, *'Knowing Me, Knowing You'* and *'Money, Money'* he knew that it was the perfect present for Doreen.

"Doreen is going to love this," Al thought as he carried the album over to the counter. *"I know that I could have had Shirley add this to one of her shopping lists, but I can get this packed up and posted tomorrow."*

The sales assistant put the album inside an HMV bag and took the payment. Al was feeling pleased with himself when he stepped out onto Oxford Street.

"Right, I'll get myself back to Lewisham, get changed and have a wander down the Sultan, who knows, maybe I'll get lucky tonight?" Al thought, chuckling to himself.

"Hey you!"

Al turned, briefly, to see a red-faced man he thought he recognised.

"Yes, you! Stop!"

Al increased his pace.

"Stop, you, stop!"

"Fucking hell," Al thought, his heart pounding against his chest. "It's that amateur wrestler I beat the shit out of in Holloway Road."

"Stop him, somebody stop him!"

Al kept his head down and ran, swerving from left to right to get through the heavy pedestrian traffic. As he was about to pass a bus that had stopped and opened its doors, Al quickly shot off to his right and got on. He paid the driver and promptly bolted upstairs where he sat on a seat close to the back and lowered his head.

"What are the fucking chances?" Al thought as he lowered his head further.

Finally, the bus moved away to join the traffic.

"Lost you!" Al thought as a victorious smile spread across his face. *"That was close. Too bloody close for comfort!"*

Al loosened the grip he had on the album and relaxed back in the seat while the bus moved steadily through central London. Fifteen minutes passed when Al heard the sound of a police siren.

"You've got to be kidding me," Al thought.

The siren sounded again.

Al rose gingerly from his seat and looked out through the back window.

"Shit, there's a police car behind us," Al thought as he sat back down. *"That can't be for me, can it?"*

The bus continued to move through the dense London traffic when Al heard the sound of several police cars. He looked up towards the front of the bus where two teenagers were pointing out of the front window.

"No, no, no," Al thought as he lowered himself down into the seat.

Outside the bus, three police cars had surrounded the bus. One vehicle behind with its lights flashing and two parked at an angle at the front to box the London bus in.

Al could hear the automatic doors open downstairs and a loud exchange of words.

"Fuck no, it can't be," Al thought as he tried desperately to lower himself even further into the seat and be inconspicuous.

Al heard the thud of boots on the stairs but kept his eyes fixed on the floor. He could feel his pulse racing and a tingling sensation in his hands. He could sense an unpleasant taste in his mouth as it dried rapidly. He felt dizzy and could feel his face, neck and upper torso begin to flush.

"This is the man!"

Al lifted his head just as a hand was placed firmly on his shoulder.

The amateur wrestler stood over Al and motioned the three police officers towards him.

"That is him!" the wrestler cried out again.

"I don't know what you're talking about," Al said as the police officers produced a set of handcuffs.

"I think you're confusing me with someone else," Al said as one of the officers grabbed him by the arm.

"You're making a dreadful mistake," Al pleaded as the placed the handcuffs on Al's' wrists.

"You need to come with us," the lead police officer said.

"I really don't understand what's going on," Al implored as they led him, handcuffed, towards the stairway.

"You can tell us all about it at the station," the officer said as he tightened his grip on Al's arm.

"I've never seen this man before in my life," Al said as he was frog-marched off the bus and bundled into the back of the police car behind the bus.

"Of course you haven't," the officer said before slamming the door shut.

"Fuck, fuck, fuck!" Al thought as he looked down at his handcuffed wrists.

The police officer pressed the button for the blue lights to commence flashing and then held the siren for several seconds before forcing his way out into the traffic. The driver used the siren to stop traffic at the traffic lights and proceeded to cross over while the lights were on red. The blue Rover P6 police car sped along until it came to a halt at the Holloway Road Police Station. The driver drove into a car park at the rear of the station. His colleague opened the rear door, took Al by the arm, led him into the station and through to the custody sergeant.

"In here," the officer said, opening a door to a small room.

Al shuffled into the room, still protesting his innocence. He was searched and his property was taken.

"This will be placed in a secure locker," the officer said as he handed Al's property to his colleague.

"Can you please take care of the ABBA album?" Al said quietly. "It's a birthday present for my sister."

"Do you have a receipt for it, sir?" the officer asked sarcastically.

"Yes, of course I do," Al said defiantly. "You'll find it amongst my other stuff."

Al was led through to an interview room where he was quizzed at length about the fight and subsequent robbery at the pub on Holloway Road, where the amateur wrestler had been left severely beaten and in urgent need of hospital care. Al maintained his innocence throughout, claiming not to know anything about the incident and stated that he'd never even met the amateur wrestler.

"If I've told you once, I've told you a hundred times," Al protested. "I'm innocent, alright!"

"You won't mind taking part in our identification parade then, will you?" the officer said with a sneer.

"No not at all," Al said, trying his best to look convincingly innocent.

An hour passed by, and an officer entered the interview room and advised the senior officer that the identity parade was ready.

Al feigned a smile, but his heart sank.

The officer led him through the police station to a larger room where he saw there were several men of similar height, build and complexion to him standing together in a line.

"Can you please join the other men in the parade," the officer said as he stepped back.

Al joined the line-up. He held his shoulders back and stood up straight so as not to look suspicious. Al immediately recognised the first witness to enter the room as the pub landlord.

"Can you please identify the man who attacked and robbed you?" the officer said.

The pub landlord looked directly at Al. He stepped forward and placed his hand on Al's shoulder.

"This is the man."

"Thank you," the officer said before leading the landlord out.

"This is a fucking nightmare!" Al thought as he watched the door open, and the landlord's wife enter the room.

Again the officer asked if the witness could identify the man who had attacked and robbed her husband that night and she immediately strutted over to Al and placed her hand firmly on his shoulder.

The officer thanked her, and she was led out of the room.

"Who the fuck are they going to wheel in next?" Al thought just as the door opened again and the amateur wrestler entered.

He didn't wait for any of the police instructions but bounded straight over to Al.

"This is him. This is the man who viciously assaulted me!" the wrestler cried out triumphantly.

The witness was led out.

"Three out of three," Al thought. *"How much worse can it get?"*

The door opened and a familiar figure entered the room.

"I don't fucking believe it," Al thought as the witness was led forward. *"That's Paul Lee, my so-called good mate, Paul Lee!"*

The officer led Paul Lee forward and asked him if he could identify the man that had been involved in the pub fight. Paul moved gingerly to the end of the line up and walked down slowly.

"You slag," Al thought. *"You fucking no good slag!"*

Paul Lee stopped by Al and placed his hand on his shoulder.

"This is the man," Paul Lee said.

Al turned so that he faced Paul Lee.

"Your witness has made a dreadful mistake," Al said through gritted teeth.

Al could see the look of sheer terror spread across Paul Lee's face. The officer promptly ushered the witness out of the room.

"You're done Lee," Al thought, tightly clenching his fists. *"You will pay for this betrayal."*

Al was removed from the identity parade and formally charged with three counts of Actual Bodily Harm (ABH), Affray, one count of Grievous Bodily Harm (GBH) and Robbery.

"I never nicked fuck all!" Al yelled after the charges were read to him.

"A man with a Scottish accent was seen to be running up the stairs of the pub with a gun and then forced the landlord to open his safe and twenty thousand pounds was stolen.

"Scottish accent, Scottish accent, just about everyone in the bloody pub was Scottish!"

"Yeah, and what was it? Oh yes, you've never seen the wrestler before," the officer said before waving his colleague over.

"Take him to the cells!"

"I am not lying," Al pleaded as they led him out of the interview room. "I had nothing to do with any robbery!"

Al was kept in the police cell overnight and then the following morning he was brought before a magistrate's court. The court was advised of his charges and that he had a warrant for his arrest in Glasgow. Bail was refused and Al was to be remanded in custody.

"I'm done," Al thought as he was brought through the back of the courts to a waiting three tonne prisoner transport vehicle. *"Bang to rights and I never nicked a bloody bean!"*

The prison van was commonly known by criminals and prison officers as a sweatbox. The truck had been converted into ten, small, lockable compartments with five units on each side of the truck. Al was still handcuffed when they led him through the narrow hallways. Al stepped into the 'sweatbox'. It was three feet by three feet and approximately seven feet high. Al sat down and looked up at the square trapdoor which could only be opened from the outside in the event of an accident. He allowed his eyes to wander over to the black twelve-inch Perspex window and then down to the three-inch gap at the bottom of the door.

"I can't believe this has happened to me," Al thought as he turned to face the black Perspex window. *"What are the fucking chances of that twat of a wrestler being in Oxford Street at exactly the same time as me? I must have been jinxed or something."*

The prison van engine started.

"We must be on the move," Al thought and let out a heavy sigh.

The van moved slowly out of the court car park and onto the main road.

"Where are they taking me?" Al wondered as the van the continued on its way.

Al looked through the black Perspex glass. It was like looking through an old sepia coloured photograph. He could see people queuing at a bus stop, chatting and holding shopping bags. Al watched as one young couple holding hands looked into the window of a children's toy shop. Suddenly, without warning, the prison van swerved abruptly to the right. Al battered his head against the window.

"What you playing at, you cunt!" an aggressive voice yelled out from another sweatbox. "What, did you get your fucking driving licence out of a kiddie's jubilee bag?"

Al rubbed the side of his head and looked back out at the hoard of people wandering in and out of the shops.

43

"Here's a joke to stop you miserable cunts from crying in your sweatbox," another prisoner yelled. "A cement mixer and a prison bus crash in central London... the old bill are advising members of the public to be on the lookout for hardened criminals."

Despite feelings of anxiety, confusion and fear of the unknown, Al chuckled to himself.

"Here's another," the prisoner yelled. "I saw a prison van full of screws repairing old shoes... I reckon it's a load of cobblers."

Al shook his head and smiled.

"Oi, comedian. Why don't you just shut the fuck up!" another prisoner shouted.

"Why don't you come and fucking make me!" the comedian yelled back aggressively.

"Your card's marked!" the second prisoner warned.

"What's the fucking matter with him?" Al thought as he looked back up at the trap door.

Without any warning the driver braked hard, and all the prisoners were plunged forward. Al hit his head for the second time.

"Oi, driver, you useless cunt. I hope your wife's boyfriend is fucking her brains out!"

"Yeah, you useless slag!"

"I need a piss!"

"How much fucking longer, you Sunday driver?"

The barrage of insults continued as the prison driver drove from Holloway to Highbury magistrate's court and then on to Kings Cross and Bow Street before heading to HMP Brixton in South London. The prison van entered Jebb Avenue at the top of Brixton Hill and stopped by the gates. Al peered out of the window and saw the

HMP Brixton Prison sign. The prison van stopped, in a wide open yard, having passed through the check point.   Al could hear the driver's keys jingling as he opened one sweat box at a time.

***

HMP Brixton is a men's prison in the London Borough of Lambeth and is operated by Her Majesty's Prison Service. It was built in 1820 and originally opened as the Surrey House of Correction. The prison was built to house one hundred and seventy prisoners. However, that number was regularly exceeded. With overcrowding, small prison cells and poor living conditions, it gained the reputation of being one of the worst prisons in London. Eventually the problem of overcrowding was addressed, and the prison expanded to house over eight hundred prisoners.

Al looked up as the driver open his door.

"This way," the driver said.

The driver led Al through the narrow hallway and out of the prison van where he was met by six uniformed screws and one senior officer. Al joined the line of prisoners and waited until the last one was taken from the prison van.

The senior prison officer stepped forward and slowly looked at the new arrivals.

"Alright lads, follow me," the senior officer said, turning abruptly on his heels and marching towards the door marked Reception.

The aroma of warm food hit Al's nostrils as he approached the door. Inside he saw a table laid out with a tray of macaroni and fresh bread. Once all ten of the prisoners were inside, the senior officer told them to help themselves to the food. Al didn't want to eat; his mind was still on the outside, so he sat down.

"I was going to the Sultan tonight," Al thought as he watched some of the prisoners fill their plates. *"Have a few drinks, game of pool and who knows... maybe a bit of skirt."*

Al looked up at the prison officers and then closed his eyes momentarily.

"FUCK!" Al thought as one of the officers closed the reception door and locked it.

"You not eating mate?"

Al looked up to a see a heavy-set lad in his mid-twenties with dark brown hair that had been parted on the side.

"Nah, I don't fancy it," Al said as the lad sat next to him.

"Billy, Billy Corrigan," Billy said in his broad Irish accent.

"Al, Al McIntosh," Al replied.

"Sad state of affairs, this," Billy said.

"Mate, you don't know the half of it," Al said.

"What are you in for, Al?" Billy said with a half grin.

"GBH, ABH, Affray, criminal damage and a fucking robbery I didn't do," Al said.

Billy shovelled the macaroni into his mouth and then took a big bite from the slice of bread. Al waited for him to stop chewing.

"What about you?"

"I was having a quiet drink in this pub and then it all goes off like some kind of Western movie with John Wayne, and my drink has gone over. So I've lumped this fella and the next thing you know the gavvers are down and I'm carted off here," Billy said.

"They had witnesses then," Al said.

"It was my bollix of a mate that grassed me up," Billy said.

"Yeah, I had one of those too," Al said with a sigh.

Once the last of the prisoners finished his food, the officers began to question them.

"McIntosh," the prison officer said.

Al nodded.

"Are you a vegetarian?"

"No."

"Religion?"

"Protestant."

"I don't have a religious bone in my body," Al thought.

The screw handed him a white card.

The white card identifies the prisoner and his prison number as a Protestant while the red card was for Catholics and is placed outside the prisoner's cell door.

"Is there anyone here you've become matey with and want to share a cell with?"

"Yeah," Al said as he looked over at Billy. "I'll share with Billy Corrigan."

Billy looked back and nodded.

Al was then led down to see the prison doctor where he was declared grade 'A' and fit for work. The screw told Al that prisoners on remand did not have to work but if they chose to, the prison system would pay them. Al declined the employment opportunity. The screws then led the new arrivals down onto the remand wing where Al and Billy were put in a cell. The door was slammed shut and locked.

Al found the smell of the recently cleaned sheets almost overpowering and they felt like cardboard. He put his hand on the bed.

"This thing is as hard as a rock," Al thought as he climbed onto the bed.

"You alright, Al?" Billy said.

"Yeah, I'm alright," Al said as he looked up at the bars covering the window.

"You done time before?" Billy asked.

"Not prison time," Al said as he stared up at the ceiling. "In approved schools and detention centres most lads are not so much worried about their real problems as by the imagined anxieties of what may or may not happen."

"What about you?" Al said as he put his hands behind his head.

"No, never," Billy said.

"Showing your emotions to people in places like this is like bleeding next to a shark," Al said.

"Do you mind if I smoke?" Billy asked.

"No, not at all," Al said as he turned to the wall at his right.

"Some dirty bastard has stuck their chewing gum on the wall," Al thought.

Al could hear Billy fumbling with a cigarette packet and then heard the strike of a match and Billy inhaling deeply.

"Never fancied smoking," Al thought as the smell of cigarette smoke rose towards him. *"It was good of Billy to ask though. I appreciate that, he's a decent fella."*

Al began to feel a tense overwhelming sensation of utter dread wash over him as the final realisation of everything that had happened, and where he was, sank in.

Chapter 4

The cell door was opened at 8.00am and Al was led down with the other prisoners to a table laid out with breakfast. There was the option of hot food, cornflakes and a vegetarian option. Al looked down at the food but just couldn't bring himself to eat anything.

"McIntosh."

"Yes," Al said as he turned to face the screw.

"You're going to see the Guvnor."

Al followed the screw off the wing and back to the reception area. The prison Guvnor sat behind a desk with two officers standing either side at the front. With an officer standing to his right, Al faced the Guvnor.

"Name and number to the Guvnor!" the officer yelled.

"You know my name, it's McIntosh and I ain't got a clue about any number."

"Your number McIntosh, your number! That's all you are in here!"

Al remained quiet for a few seconds before the prison officer reminded him of his number.

"Mr McIntosh," the Guvnor said, looking Al up and down. "Do you understand what you are in here for?"

"What do you think, I'm some kind of a fucking idiot?" Al thought.

"Yeah, three counts of ABH, one of GBH, Affray, Criminal Damage and Robbery," Al said decisively. "Oh, and by the way... I'm innocent!"

"Yes, Mr McIntosh," the Guvnor said with a sardonic smirk. "Everyone is in here."

"Keep your head down and you will have no problems," the Guvnor said, "but if you cause trouble then my officers can make life extremely difficult."

Al remained quiet.

"As a remand prisoner you are entitled to a visit every day except Sundays. You can write to friends or family and the state will pay for your postage," the Guvnor said as he leaned back in his chair. "Do you understand?"

"Yes," said Al.

"Yes, sir!" the screw to Al's right yelled.

Al turned slowly to face the screw.

"I don't call you Sir, Guvnor or bloody Boss," Al said belligerently.

"Take him back to the cells," the Guvnor ordered.

The officer that had stood to Al's right opened the door and beckoned him to move.

"We've got your number, Mac," hissed the screw as Al passed him.

"You'd best not come on your own," Al thought as he passed him. *"I'll batter seven shades of shit out of a numpty like you."*

Al was taken back to the wing where he learnt that remand prisoner's cells remained open all day while the convicted had theirs locked.

Al came to the conclusion that a smart man in his predicament accepts the circumstances and the associated pain and then endures it, while ensuring that he doesn't add to it. Over the following days and weeks, he made a point of meeting fellow prisoners and striking up conversations. Billy, his cell mate, became a good friend and had opted to take a job. Al was surprised to learn that he had taken on the role as an Altar Boy to the priest. On one occasion Al had stopped the priest talking mid-sentence and asked him why he didn't clean his heavily tobacco-stained teeth.

Al joined a group of men on the landing that were soon to all become good friends. Big Gay Roger was as skinny as a garden rake and stood a good six foot four inches tall. Al thought he had the most wonderful 'toff' accent and often thought that he could have easily passed as a lad from Cambridge or Oxford. During the daily conversations, Big Gay Roger confessed to being a con man. He would arrive at a five star up-market hotel with several expensive suitcases providing the illusion that he was a man of wealth and book a suite.

During his stay he would live a champagne lifestyle during the evenings and then, while other guests were out, he would use his skeleton keys to open the rooms of affluent guests and rob them of anything of value. After two or three weeks, Roger would do a moonlight flit and leave the hotel - and the very large bill - behind. Al was fascinated by his stories and imagined that he would have to need nerves of steel to front something like that out for so long. After two years of the millionaire lifestyle, Big Gay Roger booked into an exclusive London hotel and began to run his usual scam. However, the police were called after the first robbery and Big Gay Roger found himself being interviewed, so he told the police that he himself had also been robbed of eight thousand pounds in cash and a solid gold Rolex watch had been stolen. Big Gay Roger, with his stereotypical, over the top mannerisms and his claim had sparked the suspicions of one officer who took it upon himself to have Roger's room searched. Cash, jewellery and other stolen goods were found, leading to his arrest.

Big Gay Roger was in a relationship with an older man called Franco. Al was stunned to learn that Franco had been robbing banks on mainland Spain during the 1960s and while living the playboy lifestyle had his villa surrounded and was marched off to a jail. Franco explained that back then, under Francisco Franco, the prime minister's, regime, he could have been executed. With bribes and help from friends in Spain's criminal underworld, he managed a daring escape and sought political asylum in Great Britain. Franco explained that he missed the lifestyle that having money provided, so he set about robbing banks in England. Al watched as Franco leaned back in his seat and described the wonderful restaurants where he ate, the expensive wines and the titillating, adventurous, liaisons he had.

Al was back in the cell when Billy arrived. Once the screw slammed the door shut, Billy produced a plastic bottle with a white liquid.

"Want a swig, Al?" Billy said as he wiped the plastic bottle's rim.

"What is it?" Al said as he turned and dropped down to the floor.

"Have a taste," Billy said with a cheeky grin.

Al took the bottle, sniffed the contents and took a small swig.

"It's vodka!" Al said as he turned to Billy.

"Well go on then, take a good swig!" Billy said.

"How the hell did you get your hands on this?" Al asked before handing the bottle back to Billy.

"Now that would be telling," Billy said. "Ask no questions and I'll tell no lies."

Al and Billy drank the vodka and joked and laughed as the alcohol took effect.

The following day, just after breakfast, the priest was on the wing.

"I wonder if he's cleaned his teeth yet," Al thought as the priest approached him.

"Hello Father," Al said. "How are you today?"

"My boy there is no peace for the wicked," the priest said. "I've got to go and listen to those dirty, no-good, whores in Holloway prison this afternoon."

Al was stunned by his comments.

"They file into the confession box and tell me how they have been sucking off their best friend's boyfriend's cock or dreaming of a big black cock inside them and then have the audacity to ask for forgiveness. I'm telling you son, the almighty God fucked everything up when he created woman."

"They tell you this in the confession box?" Al said, still stunned by what he was hearing.

"That and so much more," the priest said, nodding his head enthusiastically. "Women are the scourge of society and the root cause of everything that's wrong in the world."

"I thought that whatever is said in a confession box, was, well, confidential," Al said.

The priest scrunched up his face before letting out a short chuckle.

"They tell me, and I tell some of the officers and we have a damn good laugh about it," the priest said. "You must understand, my boy, they are like pond life, utter scum to be wiped away. If I had the button to rid the world of these vile creatures, I'd press it today."

Al's jaw dropped.

"I don't believe what I'm hearing. And all this from a supposed man of God," Al thought.

"Anyway, I've not got all day. There's God's work to be done," the priest said before scurrying off down the wing.

Al spotted Big Gay Roger, Franco and another man on the landing.

"Al, this is The Mad Axe Man of Edgware Road," Big Gay Roger said as Al sat down.

"Good to meet you Al, call me Axe."

"Good to meet you too, Axe," Al said.

"You don't look like much to me, pal," Al thought as Axe continued with a story of how he and his trusty axe battled with several men in a pub brawl on the Edgware Road.

A screw called Axe away for a meeting with the Guvnor.

"Is this bloke for real?" Al said as leaned against the wall.

"Oh fuck yeah," Big Gay Roger said. "Al, I was there, and saw it with my own eyes on one occasion. He buried this axe into a lad's shoulder and there was blood everywhere. That's how he got his name... The Mad Axe man of Edgware Road."

"If it was anyone else but you telling me this, Roger, I'd think it was all bollocks," Al said. "He reels off these stories like Hans Fucking Christian Andersen."

"I can only tell you what I've seen with my own eyes," Big Gay Roger said.

"What do you think of Officer Williams, the black screw?" Franco said.

"I think he's alright as it goes," Al said.

"It's got to be tough on him," Franco said. "I mean the other screws don't like him and they don't hide it too well either."

"I heard that when Hodges' wife didn't turn up, he started to worry and told Officer Williams," Big Gay Roger said softly. "So, Officer Williams has taken it upon himself to go around to see Hodges' wife and told her how worried he was about her. I mean he didn't need to do that."

"None of this fucking lot would do something like that," Franco said, pointing at two screws chatting on the landing.

"No, they wouldn't, and in my book that makes him alright," Big Gay Roger said in his best, over-exaggerated Cambridge voice. "That man is a proper human being and could have lost his job for doing something as valiant as that."

"So, is he bent?" Al whispered. "You know, good for bringing gear in or what?"

"Absolutely not," Franco said.

"I wouldn't dream of asking him," Big Gay Roger said.

Al held both his hands up.

"I was only asking," Al said with a snigger.

Al looked up to see Billy standing outside their cell waving down to him.

"I'll see you lads later," Al said as he walked off to see Billy.

"Alright Billy, what's up?" Al said.

Billy produced another bottle from under his jumper

Al's eyes lit up and quickly turned to the cell door.

"You've got more vodka?" Al whispered with a hint of excitement in his voice.

Remand prisoners were allowed one and a half tins of beer per day or half a bottle of wine. Most prisoners chose Special Brew for its strength.

"We can get wasted tonight, mate," Billy said as he put the bottle under his pillow.

"I really don't understand how you're doing, it, but good on you mate," Al said as he slapped Billy on the forearm.

56

Al turned to see Prison Officer Williams standing by the cell door.

"Can I help you?" Al said with a half-smile.

"Would you lads like to paint your cell?"

"Do what?" Billy said as he approached the officer.

"New regulations; remand prisoners have the option to paint their cells," Officer Williams said. "So, what's it to be?"

"Yeah, alright," Al said as his smile spread further across his face. "What are the colour choices?

"Red, blue, green, cream, yellow... whatever you want," Officer Williams said with a broad grin.

"I reckon red," Al said as he turned to Billy.

Billy shrugged his shoulders.

"Red is good by me."

"Leave it with me lads, and I'll get you some paint and brushes," Officer Williams said before moving on to the next cell.

"Whatever next?" Billy said.

"I don't know, maybe a juke box, pool table and a well-stocked bar with a pretty young barmaid with legs that go right up to her armpits," Al said.

"Yeah, right, dream on," Billy said with a hollow laugh.

Once Al and Billy were locked in their cells, they made light work of the Special Brew before Billy brought out the vodka.

"Billy, have you got someone on the firm for this or what?" Al said as he handed Billy the bottle. "What I mean, is this an ongoing arrangement?"

"Yeah, it can be," Billy said before taking a long swig from the bottle. "It's a kind of trade."

"Look, if there's money or something, I'll pay my way," Al said.

"Nah, nothing like that, and besides you're a mate so I'm happy to share it with you," Billy said as he wiped the rim and passed it back to Al.

"I appreciate it and your friendship," Al said before taking a huge gulp.

There was silence for a few moments.

"I get it from the priest," Billy said.

"What?" Al said as he sat bolt upright. "You're kidding me!"

Billy shook his head.

"Like I said it's a kind of trade," Billy said. "I fuck him, Al."

"What did you just say?" Al said as his jaw dropped open.

"He asked me to fuck him in the confession box and in return I get this vodka," Billy said calmly.

"So, are you gay?" Al asked before taking a small sip from the vodka bottle and handing it back to Billy.

Billy shook his head.

"Nah, I'm not gay at all but I do like a drop of vodka," Billy said.

"Billy, I don't know how you do it but I'm grateful for the vodka," Al said.

"Like I said, Al. it's just a trade. It means nothing," Billy said.

***

The following morning the priest was on the wing.

"Look at that!" the priest cried out as he pointed to a picture of a Page Three model that had been cut out from a Sun newspaper and stuck to the cell wall with chewing gum.

There was a radio on in the cell playing '*I feel Love*' by Donna Summer.

"What?" Al said, shrugging his shoulders.

"That picture of a naked woman on the wall," the priest said continuing to point aggressively at the picture. "Do you really think that's right?"

"You're being fucked where the sun don't shine by my cell mate in the confession box and you have the front to ask if some poor bastard is doing wrong by having a picture of a Page Three girl on his wall," Al thought. *"You, mate, are a hypocrite of the worst kind!"*

Al took another look at the picture from the cell door.

"That's the lovely Maureen Flanagan," Al said as he turned back to face the priest. "Every red-blooded male loves Maureen Flanagan."

The priest spluttered and failed to start his sentence before he turned sharply and continued to strut along the wing.

Al joined Big Gay Roger, Franco and Axe at their usual spot on the landing. After listening to several more of Axe's stories, Al interrupted.

"So what are you in here for, Axe?" Al asked.

Big Gay Roger's eyes lit up and Franco slowly shook his head.

Axe turned to Al and lowered his head.

"It ain't for sorting people out with an axe," Axe muttered.

"So, what is it?"

Al could see that Big Gay Roger was wincing as the words left Al's lips.

"It's my old woman, the other half," Axe said as he looked sharply from left to right. "Look we've been together for a while, you know, and sex was becoming a bit... predictable. So, one night we watched this blue movie and had a few drinks and I persuaded her to let me fuck her up the jacksie."

Al jolted upright as did Big Gay Roger and Franco.

"Anyway, I sunk my old cock in there and it was like having it clamped in a vice. The old woman winced, moaned and fucking cried but I just fucked her rigid" Axe said.

"This is getting interesting," Al thought.

"Well now I've got a raging taste for the brown box and so I was coming home from work and the thought of my cock stuck in her cute little ass had me excited, so I would come in, bend her over the dining room table and just fuck the life out of her."

"Poor woman," Big Gay Roger said with a half-smile.

"In fairness, she begged me not to do it saying that my cock was too big for a place like that but once that image came into my head, I just had to have some," Axe said.

"So what happened?" Al asked, listening intently.

"I'm on my way home and I'm thinking that I'm going to fuck her little brown box on the stairs when the old bill have swooped in and arrested me on the front drive."

"No way," Franco said.

"Yeah, they stuck me in handcuffs, the whole nine yards," Axe said, shrugging his shoulders.

"But what did they nick you for?" Al asked.

"Julie, that's my wife, said she had had enough of the torture and walking around like John Wayne, so she reported me for raping her anally."

"Can they do you for raping your wife?" Franco asked.

"You better believe it," Axe said. "I was nicked, magistrates and then shipped off to here."

"Have you seen your wife since?" Al asked.

"Oh yeah, she visits me every day," Axe said.

"What, are you kidding?" Al said in disbelief. "What do you talk about?"

"She told me that the only reason she went to the police was that she needed to give her little brown box a rest."

Al bit his lip to avoid laughing out loud.

"Can't she just drop the charges?" Franco asked

"We've been talking about that and yesterday she made me promise never to touch her bum again," Axe said as he shrugged his shoulders. "I promised, but made the mistake of saying that it was only because it was just so tight compared to the other place."

Al gasped.

"That wouldn't have gone down well," he said.

"It didn't. She started going on about me saying that she was loose and saggy which, of course, I didn't mean. It was just, well, better the other way," Axe said as he leant back. "She got up and said that eleven-inch cocks were abnormal, and women were not made to take things that big in the ass. Then she picked up her handbag and stormed off and visiting wasn't even over."

"I've never heard anything like this in my life," Al thought as he tried desperately not to laugh.

"Do you have the deposition?" Big Gay Roger said with one raised eyebrow.

Axe nodded.

"Would you mind if I read it?" Big Gay Roger said.

"Me too," Franco said.

"Why, do you think it might help?" Axe asked.

"You never know," Big Gay Roger said with a wry smile.

"You boys are going to get yourselves off on reading that," Al thought.

Chapter 5

"Here, Al, have you read Axe's deposition?" Billy said as he held it from his bed.

"No, not yet." Al said as he put his hands in his pockets and leaned up against the cell wall. "I thought it was only Big Gay Roger and Franco that had read it."

"This is fucking hysterical mate. It reads like a porn magazine. His wife has described his old todger right down to how many bleeding veins he has," Billy said with a raucous laugh. "According to this, Axe's dick is so large it has its own post code."

"Did you know he's been banged up in here for three months and she's visited him every day," Al said.

"You couldn't make shit like this up," Billy said.

"You need to get that back to Big Gay Roger," Al said.

"Mate this deposition has done the rounds. Just about everyone has read it," Billy said as he put it on the bed.

"McIntosh, Corrigan," Al turned to see Officer Williams standing by the cell entrance. "I've got some bad news, lads."

"What?" Billy said.

"It's the red."

"What red?" Al said as he shrugged his shoulders.

"This red," Officer Williams said, pointing to the recently painted cell.

"We've just painted this, and you said any colour we like," Al said defensively.

"I know, lads, but it's not my call," Officer Williams said as he rubbed his hand over the red painted wall. "Upstairs they think that the colour red could, psychologically, make the prisoners violent so it has to be changed."

There were a few moments silence as Al looked from Williams to his cell mate Billy.

"What about black?" Al asked.

"Black is good with me," Billy said.

"Good," Officer Williams said with a broad smile. "I'll organise some black paint and brushes."

"Has visiting time finished?" Al said as he looked past Officer Williams and onto the wing.

Officer Williams looked down at his watch.

"About five minutes," Officer Williams replied before turning sharply and walking off down the wing.

"I'll catch you later, Billy" Al said as he headed to the cell door.

"Yeah, I'll have some more vodka later," Billy whispered.

"I don't know how you do it, mate," Al thought as he left the cell. *"You ain't even gay!"*

"Alright Al," a voice called out as he passed by the adjoining cell.

"Yeah, you?" Al said as he stopped and looked in.

"Have you got to change your cell colour too?" the con asked.

Al entered the cell and began to nod.

"Oh, I'm sorry," Al said as he averted his eyes from a photograph of a naked woman on his cell wall.

"Oh, that's alright, Al," the con said. "It's Doreen, my wife."

"You've got a picture of your naked wife on your wall," Al said as he turned his back on the photograph. "Anyone could walk in here and see her. Doesn't that bother you?"

"Nah," the con said with a chuckle. "She's a good-looking woman and sexy as fuck. Sometimes I let a few lads on the wing borrow the pic, you know, to sort themselves out."

"And you're alright with that?" Al said with a look of astonishment.

"Yeah, why not?" the con said. "We've always been kind of open about things like that."

"What, your wife knows that you let other guys see her naked?" Al said as his jaw dropped.

"Oh yeah and during the visits I'll tell her who has borrowed the photo," the con said with a grin. "She likes that... we both do."

"I suppose it takes all sorts," Al said as he turned slowly to see the photograph.

"We have taken it a bit further, you know, when I was on the out," the con said. "We did meet up with this one guy from an advert we placed in the back of a magazine.

"You let some bloke fuck your missus?" Al said incredulously.

"Don't get me wrong, I'm not some sissy boy who wants cuckolding. Doreen and I have both had fantasies and as adults we took it one step further. We're both secure in our relationship but wanted to push boundaries and not be confined by what society deems normal," the con said.

"So, when it was all done, the bloke just left and that was it? Were you worried that she might just fall for this bloke and leave you?" Al said.

"We spent an afternoon exploring our sexuality without rules or expectations and then the guy just left, and we fucked like rabbits for a month after when we talked about everything that had happened. The thing is, Al, I do not own my wife any more than she owns me. I cannot make her love or stay with me. That would be her choice and what we do is for us a joint experience, there is no emotional attachment to the third party," the con said.

"Well, if it works for you," Al said with a couple of shrugs.

"Are you sure you don't want to borrow the photo?" the con said. "My Doreen would like you."

"Nah, I'm good," Al said. "I'll see you later."

"I can't fucking believe what I've just heard," Al thought as he stepped down onto the landing.

Al spotted Big Gay Roger and Franco at their usual spot.

"Alright, Al," Franco said.

Al joined them.

"You waiting for the next instalment from Axe?" Big Gay Roger said with a husky laugh.

"It helps break up the day," Al said as he peered over Franco's shoulder and spotted Axe.

"He's here," Al said.

Big Gay Roger stood up and waved Axe over to join them.

"You look a bit pissed off Axe," Franco said as he moved to let Axe stand between them all.

"Yeah, I am a bit hacked off," Axe said.

"Why, what's up?" Big Gay Roger said, winking slyly at Al.

"It's the old woman," Axe said with a heavy sigh.

"What, didn't she visit?" Franco said.

66

"Oh, yeah, she visited alright, and I made all the promises she asked for. When I asked her why she hadn't been down and dropped the charges she's just said that I was convincing but then she thought about her poor brown box and she couldn't do it," Axe said, shaking his head.

Al bit his lip as he saw a wicked grin spread across Big Gay Roger's face.

"Three months I've been banged up in here," Axe said. "I've promised, and I mean it, I really do. All she has to do is drop the charges and that's it. I'll be out there, and we can just get on with life again."

Axe looked up as a black fella with long dreadlocks passed the end of the table.

"Oi, Leroy! Where's my money for the snout?" Axe called, stepping away from the group.

"Alright man," the con said. "I'll get the money from my girl during visiting tomorrow."

Axe took a couple of steps closer to the con.

"Well that's no fucking good, is it?" Axe hissed. "You fucking owe what you owe and today is pay day."

"I told you, man," the con said. "I'll sort you out tomorrow after visiting time."

"You fucking owe me today!" Axe yelled.

"Well fuck you then," the con said as he turned to face Axe. "If you want to start all that then you'll get fuck all!"

"Really? I bet you wouldn't say that to my mate Al," Axe said.

Al felt liked he'd just been slapped in the face and turned sharply.

"Are you some kind of a cunt, Axe?" Al said as he strode towards him. "Who the fuck do you think you are putting my name in the frame?"

"I just thought...?" Axe said.

"What, you thought I'd do your fucking dirty work for you?" Al said as he took two steps closer and clenched both his fists.

"I didn't mean anything by it," Axe said as he lowered his head.

"Fucking Mad Axeman of Edgware Road," Al thought as he looked Axe up and down. *"You ain't nothing!"*

"I'm sorry Al," Axe said as he stepped backwards, turned and scurried off down the wing.

"Oh well that will be last of the anal adventures of the Mad Axeman then," Big Gay Roger said in his best Cambridge voice.

"I don't like that," Al said.

"Fair enough," Franco said.

"I might go and get a reading from Medium Harry," Big Gay Roger said, rubbing his hands together. "Coming?"

"Medium Harry?" Al said with a quizzical expression.

"Oh, he's good," Big Gay Roger said as they walked along the wing.

"What does he do then?"

"Harry is the kind of psychic that can communicate with the spirit world using his extrasensory perception."

"Oh, right," Al said.

"No really, Al. Harry really can receive messages and warnings from friends, family and loved ones that have passed on," Big Gay Roger said, turning as he walked. "There are angels and even spirit guides."

"Sounds like a load of bollocks to me," Al thought as he followed his friends.

"So dead people talk to him?" Al said.

"Harry will set the right ambience to conduct a reading and then use his divine powers to connect with the spirits of loved ones that have passed over," Big Gay Roger said, as he increased his pace.

"And you believe all that," Al said.

"I'm very spiritual," Big Gay Roger said firmly. "There are different types of mediums. Some communicate telepathically and tune in to the spirit world so they can listen, sense and see what the spirits are trying to tell them."

"They don't actually hear them but rather interpret what they're trying to say," Franco said.

"So, you believe in all this too?" Al said.

Franco nodded.

"There is a lot more to this realm than you can imagine," Franco said.

"They don't hear their voices then?" Al said.

"Well, some can," Big Gay Roger said. "That's what I meant by different types of medium. "Some interpret gestures, while others can hear them as clearly as you and I talking."

"What are the other ways for them to communicate?" Al asked.

"Some mediums are open to what's called 'channelling' and that's when the medium will leave their body and allow the spirit to enter it, control and speak through it," Big Gay Roger said.

"Sounds like a load more bollocks to me," Al thought. *"When you're dead, you're dead."*

The three men stopped outside a cell where they saw Medium Harry sitting at one end of his bed and another con sitting at the other. They stood in silence while Medium Harry conducted his reading.

"I can see a figure behind, you," Medium Harry said as he peered over the con's shoulder. "I can see a figure, a little girl. Would that mean something to you?"

Al watched as the con nodded his head.

"This little girl has only been in the spirit world a short time," Medium Harry said.

Al watched as the guy began to look visibly stressed.

"I can hear a name," Medium Harry said, touching his right ear. "Would Becky mean anything?

The con nodded.

Al spotted a tear run down the con's cheek.

"Ah, yes, it's Rebecca," Medium Harry said. "She would have been about seven or eight years of age when she passed."

The con wiped several tears away on his shirt sleeve.

"Rebecca is now standing by your side," Medium Harry said. "She's a pretty little girl with golden hair in pig tails."

The con became choked up as tears streamed down his face.

"She's now sitting on your lap and looking up at her daddy," Medium Harry said. "Rebecca is saying that she didn't want to die, and she misses her daddy."

The con jumped off the bed and bolted out of the cell with tears streaming down his face. He pushed past Franco and scuttled down the wing.

Al stepped into the cell and closed the door on Big Gay Roger and Franco.

"This is a fucking con!" Al said firmly.

"Some believe in the spirit world, and some don't," Medium Harry answered casually.

"You're a fucking low life con artist playing on people's emotions, and you need to stop this," Al said, his eyes burning into Mediums Harry's.

"People have reached out to mediums and psychics for hundreds of years for guidance and comfort. I have the gift to speak with the deceased, predict future events and give an insight into a person's past, present and future," Medium Harry said, holding Al's stare.

"You do this for tobacco," Al said, "You don't give a toss about that con and you're using his dead daughter to play on his emotions, and I don't fucking like it!"

"I provide a level of comfort to those who need it," Medium Harry said. "Besides, what has it got to do with you?"

"I don't like to see fraudsters like you feed off and take advantage of fellow cons," Al said. "It ain't fucking right. If I see or hear of you spinning that fella some old shit again I'll fucking do you. Now look me in the eyes and tell me I'm fucking joking!"

***

Three days later, while Al was walking along the landing, he spotted Big Gay Roger and Franco chatting with someone he thought he recognised.

"I know you," Al thought. *"I can't put my finger on it, but I have definitely seen you about."*

"It's Al, isn't it?" the con said.

71

"Yeah, that's right," Al said as he arrived at the group's usual spot on the landing. "I thought I recognised you but couldn't put a name to a face."

"I'm Carol. You were good friends with Mae West," Carol said as he held out his hand.

"Good to meet you," Al said with a broad smile. "Any friend of Mae's is a friend of mine."

***

Al had absconded from Thornley Park Approved School in Glasgow in 1969 and had made his way down South in search of his dream to move to London. Penniless, hungry and sleeping rough on a park bench in Regents Park, he spotted two men dressed as women pass him by. At first he was shocked, but saw it was Ian Jones, a lad he thought he recognised from the approved school. Ian dismissed his approach at first, but within a few steps turned back and asked if he was on the run. Al nodded and was then introduced to Mae West and Jean Harlow over some much needed fish and chips. They told Al they were male prostitutes and operated out of Soho and the West End. Mae wrote down the address of a squat in Finsbury Park and gave him a job placing cards advertising their services in telephone boxes around the West End. Al, Mae West and Jean Harlow became good friends.

"How is Mae?" Al asked.

"I've not seen Mae or Jean in a while," Carol said, feigning sorrow.

"I heard you had to re-paint your cell," Franco said.

"Yeah, apparently they think the colour red will make us violent," Al said with a chuckle. "So, we've painted it black."

"Black," Big Gay Roger said.

"Yeah, it looks pretty good actually... for a cell," Al said.

"I'll catch you later," Al said as he stepped away. "Billy is off to court in the morning."

"What are his chances?" Franco said.

"Hopefully a slap on the wrist, but you never know," Al said.

Al bounded up the stairs and entered what he thought was his cell.

"Oh, sorry mate," Al said as he saw the back of a guy going through some belongings.

Al left the cell and then looked around at where he was.

"Hold up, that's my fucking cell!" Al thought as he stomped back into the cell.

"Peter Thief!" Al yelled as he threw a mighty left hook and caught the thief squarely on the chin. He quickly fired a succession of left and right jabs. As the thief lost his balance, Al launched a right uppercut that sent him sprawling to the cell floor.

A prison thief was known amongst the cons as a 'Peter'.

"Fucking Peter Thief!" Al yelled out again as he fired one savage kick after another into the thief.

Al turned to the cell door as he heard the thundering of boots approaching his cell. Several red-faced, furious cons burst into the cell and began kicking the thief. One con reached down and grabbed the thief by the hair and dragged him, crying and screaming out onto the landing where several more cons proceeded to kick and stomp on the thief until he lay unconscious. The angry mob of hate-filled cons dispersed as the prison officers approached.

No cons were prosecuted for the violent incident. Peter Thieves, along with rapists and those who committed sexual offences against children were the most hated men in prison. A man who stole from fellow convicts paid with violence.

Al bent down and removed his toothbrush and a letter from his sister from the motionless body. He rose to his feet and stepped back from the body.

The new screw, Craig, looked at the beaten up con and then back at his two fellow officers.

"This could cost me," Al thought. *"Peter Thief or not, I'm still not fucking grassing you."*

"Let's get this slag out of here," Craig said as he pointed to the Peter Thief.

Everyone, including prison officers, hated Peter Thieves.

"What the fuck would he want with my toothbrush and a personal letter?" Al thought as he stepped into his cell. *"Fair play to the new screw, Craig, he seems alright…. for a screw."*

Billy returned to their cell shortly after the incident.

"Fuck me Al, it's all been going on here." Billy said as he stepped into his cell. "The lads said you kicked the shit out of a Peter Thief."

Al nodded and rubbed his knuckles.

"Craig, that new screw, told me that the slag was screaming out to be put on 'Rule 43'," Billy said as he reached into his jacket and produced a small plastic bottle.

Al beamed as he recognised it as being vodka.

Prison Rule 43 provides segregation when the prison authorities consider it necessary to maintain good order and discipline. Inmates can also request it for their own protection.

Al and Billy chatted and drank Special Brew and vodka until the early hours.

"My brother Brian will be twenty-one this week which means he'll be transported here for the trial," Al said. "If you can, will you please keep my cell free so that Brian can be moved in with me?"

Officer Williams hesitated and then smiled.

"I'll do what I can," Officer Williams said. "I've got some more bad news."

"More?" Al said.

"Yes, it's the colour you've painted the cell," Officer Williams said.

"What? It's black," Al said.

"I know it's frustrating, but the psychologists upstairs believe that black is just too depressing and could lead to a spate of suicides," Officer Williams said.

"For fuck's sake, why don't the head shrinks upstairs think all this shit through before we paint the bloody cells," Al thought.

"Tell you what," Al said. "I'll paint it back to the original cream."

Chapter 6

Al and Billy were sitting in their cell when they heard on the radio in the adjoining cell that Elvis Presley had died.

"Did you hear that?" Al said as he shot off the bed and onto his feet.

"What?" Billy said, looking confused.

Al bolted out of the cell and stood by the door of the adjoining cell.

"Can you turn that up, mate?" Al called out.

The con reached over and turned the radio volume up.

'Elvis Presley, aged 42, has died at his Memphis Mansion today'

"Not the King," Billy said as he joined his cellmate.

"I can't believe it," Al said as he remembered his aunts, Doreen and Mary dancing in their high heels to the rock 'n' roll tracks at their home when he was a child.

"It's the end of an era," Billy said.

"No one will ever forget the 16th of August, 1977," Al said.

Al and Billy returned to their cell where they talked about their favourite songs and how they loved to dance to Elvis. Once the cells were locked up, Al and Billy began to sing 'Heartbreak Hotel' by Elvis Presley at the top of their voices to celebrate the passing of the King of Rock 'n' Roll.

It wasn't long before every con in every cell on the remand wing joined in and sang 'Jailhouse Rock' at the top of their voices.

***

The new screw, Craig, had given Al the heads up that his brother, Brian, was being processed and would shortly be on the wing. Al waited on the landing. He was looking forward to seeing his brother after so long. The door opened and Al could feel a sense of excitement wash over him. The first con to enter the wing was George Davis.

"That's the bank robber, George Davis," Al thought as he waited patiently. *"I've seen the 'George Davis is Innocent' graffiti painted on walls in London."*

George Davis was an armed robber from Bletchley who was convicted in 1975, for an armed payroll robbery at The London Electricity Board offices in Ilford. Friends and supporters launched the 'George Davis is Innocent' campaign as the conviction was based solely on unreliable use of identification evidence. George Davis was released on the orders of Home Secretary, Roy Jenkins, in May 1976. Following an armed bank raid on the Bank of Cyprus on the Seven Sisters Road on the 23rd of September 1977, George Davis was caught at the wheel of the getaway vehicle with weapons besides him.

"Brian!" Al thought as his brother stepped onto the wing.

Al rushed forward and shook his brother's hand.

"Good to see you!" Al said.

After the brothers caught up, Al took him down on the wing and introduced him to Big Gay Roger, Franco and Carol.

"The guvnor has banned the use of Ouija boards," Big Gay Roger said with a look of complete disgust.

The Ouija board is also known as a spirit board. It's a flat board marked with the letters of the alphabet, the numbers 0-9, and the words Yes and No. The prison inmates would place their fingers on a clear plastic glass, used to dispense medication, to spell out messages from spirits.

"Good, I don't like shit like that," Al said.

"It can be dangerous," Franco said. "I've heard stories of demonic possession."

"No," Big Gay Roger said, shaking his head emphatically. "It's a tool for positivity."

"Well that should fuck Medium Harry up," Al said through partially gritted teeth.

"You shouldn't be so hard on him, Al," Big Gay Roger said. "He's done a lot of good for morale on the wing. Like it or not, there are those, me included, that believe our friends and family are on the other side looking out for us."

"It's all bollocks and you'll never convince me otherwise," Al thought.

"It doesn't matter what the Governor orders, because no one in here gives a fuck anyway," Big Gay Roger said before lighting a rolled cigarette.

The conversation turned to legendary criminals from the 1950s when Carol spoke out.

"I worked for the Messina Brothers," Carol said.

"Wasn't it them that established the sex trade in the West End?" Big Gay Roger said.

Carol nodded his head.

"I can remember when Edward Messina first moved to London with his French wife, Colette," Carol said as all eyes fell on him. "She had been a prostitute."

"Really?" Brian said.

"Oh yes," Carol said. "She was quite the driving force in the early days."

"They were Maltese, weren't they?" Franco asked.

"Yes," Carol said, nodding. "Once Edward and Colette were up and running, Edward sent for his brothers, Charles, Alfred, Arthur and Raymond and that's when things really started to heat up. The brothers were importing women from Belgium, France and Spain to feed London's appetite for whores."

"I've read newspaper articles but never knew how big they got," Big Gay Roger said.

"It wasn't long before they started to recruit young English girls to work the streets for them. At their peak they had over two hundred of the most expensive high-class prostitutes working the West End for them. They were extremely powerful and had a lot of the police on the payroll."

"How much were the girls allowed to keep?" Brian asked, listening intently.

"The street girls were expected to bed seven punters a day, seven days a week and they got to keep just twenty per-cent of the day's takings," Carol said.

"Fuck that," Brian said.

"The Messina brothers didn't fuck about," Carol said. "I witnessed one poor girl get slashed across the face with a razor because she was falling behind. If you didn't earn, you got cut."

"Dirty, rotten, evil bastards," Al muttered.

"So, what did you do for them?" Big Gay Roger said.

"I'm a male prostitute," Carol said frankly. "Not many people know this, but the Messina brothers didn't just run female sex rings. They also had people like me for the more discerning clientele."

"You mean politicians and people from television," Al said.

Carol nodded.

"I saw it in Soho when I was carding for Mae West and Jean Harlow," Al said.

"What happened to the Messina Brothers?" Brian asked. "It sounds like they had things pretty well tied up."

"They got complacent, and it didn't help their cause when Raymond was supposed to have said to somebody in the press that the Messinas were more powerful than the British Government and followed it up by saying that they do whatever they want in England."

"That wouldn't have gone down well with the establishment," Big Gay Roger said.

"It didn't, and some crime journalist from 'The People' newspaper began writing articles. It wasn't long before Scotland Yard got involved and they were forced to flee the country," Carol said.

"Who took over?" Brian asked. "Someone always steps in."

"That would have been Bernie Silverman," Al said firmly. "I ran bits and pieces for him a few years back when I was a kid."

"Carol," Brian said. "How did you end up in here?"

Carol smiled.

"I would meet with men in bars that catered for men that liked the company of other men," Carol explained. "Then, when the punter was ready, we would go back to their home. Once safely inside and when things were about to hot up, I would produce a tool and start beating the fuck out of them while ordering them to open their safe and give me their money. Most of these men are living a lie and had a wife and kids, so I thought I would be pretty safe. Even if they reported the robbery to the police, they are unlikely to admit to bringing home a male prostitute for sex... Well, that was the plan until one did exactly that, and the next thing I know I've been set about by three coppers and then I'm banged up in here awaiting a trial."

"Fuck!" Brian sighed.

"It's never good to judge a book by its cover," Carol said as he turned to face Brian. "Especially in a place like this."

"Is it alright if I join you?"

The group looked up to see a smartly dressed guy in his early thirties with highlights in his blonde hair.

"I'm sure no one will mind if my friend Alan joins us," Carol said.

Alan smiled awkwardly.

"I'm Alan, Alan Conroy."

One by one the group introduced themselves.

"What are you in for?" Brian said.

"Armed robbery," Alan said. "But I didn't do it."

"Of course you didn't, Alan, we're all innocent in here," Al said with a chuckle.

***

Brian, like Al and every prisoner that entered Brixton prison on remand, was given the choice of taking a job working for a wage. Unlike his brother, he agreed to the work believing that it would help the time to pass. Brian had been given the job, with extra pay, in 'Bomb Disposal'.

Once the cell doors are slammed and locked up for the night any prisoner needing the toilet would either have to relieve himself in the piss pot or pass excrement onto a sheet of tissue paper and then throw the package out of the barred window. Prisoners who couldn't sleep would lie awake all night as the sound of shit parcels splatted down on the ground. The cleaning up job from the night's activity was known as 'Bomb Disposal'.

Four weeks later:

Alan Conroy had stopped by Al's cell.

"Do you want to trade this Special Brew?" Alan said as held up a full tin.

"Yeah, sure," Al said as he reached behind the bunk and produced a new tube of toothpaste.

Al and Brian had set up trade deals with cons on the wing with Special Brew for toothpaste, cakes or biscuits. Every night the brothers would drink five or six tins and chat about what they would do once they were outside. There was some concern when a couple of inmates attacked the screws after drinking heavily.

"Do you mind if I ask you something?" Al said.

"Fire away," Alan said.

"It's none of my business and I'm not judging but... are you and Carol, well, together?" Al asked with a hint of awkwardness.

Alan sighed heavily.

"Look, I'm sorry for asking. I should have kept my mouth shut," Al said.

"Nah, it's alright Al," Alan said as he stepped further into the cell. "I'm not ashamed or bothered. Yeah, we're together but I'm not gay."

"You're not gay, so how does that work?" Al said sitting up.

"We started chatting and I just thought that she's had a really rough life, you know, a proper sob story and I felt sorry for her."

"You called Carol her," Al thought.

"Things just went from there and I suppose you could say I fell for her," Alan said as he shrugged his shoulders. "We are an item, a couple."

"Like I said, Alan, I'm not judging, I was just curious," Al said.

"Carol wants us to work together when we get out," Alan said.

"What, robbing banks or pimping Carol out?" Al thought.

"I know what you're thinking, but we're going to start some kind of business and leave our pasts behind," Alan said.

"Good for you mate," Al said with a warm, genuine, smile. "Everyone deserves to be happy and it's no one's business what happens between two consenting adults."

"Yeah, that's what we think," Alan said. "Besides, if someone pisses either of us off, I'll fucking do them. Catch you later, Al."

"I hope it all works out for them," Al thought as he lay back on his bed.

Al looked up as Brian entered the cell. He reached for his nose as the strong smell of shit assaulted his nostrils.

"Brian, you stink of shit!"

"Yeah, I know," Brian said.

"Well go and get a fucking shower then," Al said, fanning his nostrils with his right hand.

"The showers aren't working," Brian said, stepping closer.

"For fuck's sake, Brian, you're stinking this fucking cell out!"

"You'd better stop with that," Brian said with a hint of agitation in his voice. "I told you the showers aren't working!"

Al began fanning his nostrils faster as the lingering smell of shit began to envelop his entire face.

Brian looked down at his brother and screwed up his face in anger.

"I'm telling you, Al. I'm not fucking scared of you!"

Al let out a short, harsh, laugh.

"I'll fucking sort you out like I have all my life," Al said as he continued to fan his face.

The tension between the two brothers continued to mount as Brian's face became increasingly contorted as Al fanned his face.

"Say it one more time and I'll fucking do you!" Brian said as he clenched both fists.

"Brian... Fuck off," Al said as he rose from the bed. "Oh, by the way... you stink like shit!"

Brian yelled and threw a punch.

Al absorbed the punch and threw a right cross, followed by a left hook and an uppercut that had Brian stagger backwards against the wall. With the adrenaline racing through his body, Al continued his assault with a series of jabs, hooks and a second uppercut that found Brian's chin.

BANG!

Al stepped back for a second as Brian, still throwing his fists aimlessly, slid down the wall. He launched several kicks that lifted Brian's body off the cell floor before turning around and picking up a scrubbing brush.

"You think you can fucking talk to me like that?" Al yelled as he pounded the scrubbing brush relentlessly into Brian's bloodied face. "I'll scrub your fucking mouth out!"

Al grabbed his brother around the throat with one hand and continued to batter his face with the other.

SMACK! SMACK! SMACK! SMACK!

"Mercy, mercy, I'm your brother, I'm your brother," Brian cried.

"Fuck mercy!" Al replied as the rage continued to boil while he battered his brother's face over and over with the wooden scrubbing brush.

SMACK! SMACK! SMACK!

"Al, Al," Brian cried.

Al stopped momentarily and glanced down at the blood on his hands and his brother's savagely beaten face.

"Fuck me, I could have killed my brother," Al thought.

***

Brian stayed in their cell the following day while Al wandered down to join his friends, Big Gay Roger, Franco and Alan Conroy at their usual spot on the landing.

"You, Mr McIntosh, have been the talk of the wing," Big Gay Roger said. "The word is that if you can do that to your own brother what the fuck would you do to one of us?"

"You've gained quite the reputation," Franco said.

"How is Brian?" Big Gay Roger asked cautiously.

"My brother is a game fucker and he ain't scared of anyone," Al said firmly. "Give him a couple of days and he'll be back on the wing."

Two men strolled over and introduced themselves as Bobby and Ben. They were father and son. It wasn't long before the men engaged them in conversation and Alan asked what they were in for.

"I was an officer in the British Army," Bobby said as he pulled his shoulders back. "I was stationed in Saudi Arabia and I'm fluent in Arabic."

"Arabic. That must be a tough language to master," Al said.

"My son and I took it one stage further and we mastered the different dialects which helped to get us in with the rich and powerful," Bobby said.

"It was going well for a while," Ben said.

"What happened?" Alan said as he leaned across the table.

"We did a job on this one fella," Bobby said. "Sixty thousand pounds and all in cash."

"Fuck me," Alan said. "That's more than most blaggers pull on an armed bank robbery."

"Not that you would know," Al said with a chuckle. "Because you're innocent, right?"

Everyone in the group began to laugh.

"It was a blinding score," Bobby said, "Right up until the moment the authorities swooped in."

"I heard that they don't take shit like that too lightly in Saudi," Franco said.

"Yeah, I was shitting myself, to be honest. They will cut your hands off over there for stealing," Bobby said.

Alan looked down at Bobby's hands.

"So what happened to you then?"

"I was lucky. The authorities didn't want any bad press from some Englishman having his hands chopped off, so I was deported and my son, Ben, followed me back to England where we went back to work here in London."

"It was sweet while it lasted," Ben said.

"We would dress as Arabs and then follow the real rich Arabs into the West End Hotels. When it came to booking in, they immediately assumed that we were all together, apologised for the mix up and gave us a suite," Bobby said.

"That's when the fun started," Ben said.

"Yes, we'd wait for the other Arabs to leave their room and then break into the safe and rob them blind," Bobby said.

"Watches, jewellery, cash, all sorts," Ben said.

"The money was rolling in. Until the last job," Bobby said.

"What happened?" Big Gay Roger asked, hanging on their every word.

"We emptied the safes and then bolted down the back stairs, still dressed as Arabs, and out of the fire exit only to be met by a mob of old bill," Bobby said. "We tried blagging it, but they knew and were waiting for us."

"That's a right proper shame," Alan said. "A nice, clean bit of work and good money."

"There are a couple of bully boys on the wing, Al, taking some of the lad's beer and wine," Big Gay Roger said.

"That's not my business," Al said resolutely, "until it impacts my business."

Al left the group and was stopped on his way back to the cell by the new screw, Craig.

"Have you heard anything about me on the wing?" Craig whispered.

"Do you mean that you're a cousin to Charlie Campbell?" Al replied. "It's just a rumour that's going around."

"Shit," Craig hissed slowly shaking his head.

"This can't get back or I'll definitely lose my job," Craig said.

Charlie Campbell was known by the authorities and those in criminal circles as a notorious and extremely violent bank robber.

"If anyone says anything to me I'll shoot it down as bullshit," Al said with a wink.

"Cheers," Craig replied with a half-smile. "Do you think you'll get a not guilty?"

"No, I'm done," Al said.

"You've got an outstanding warrant in Glasgow, right?" Craig said.

Al nodded.

"If you get a guilty in court, write to the Director of Public Prosecutions in Glasgow and plead guilty to the charges. There's a good chance they'll drop the charges, but only if you have been found guilty," Craig said.

"Are you sure about this?" Al asked.

Craig nodded.

"Nothing is cast iron but there's a good chance you'll walk away from it, but you do have to be in the nick when you write."

"Thanks, I appreciate that," Al said.

Chapter 7

Al and Brian had spent the day chatting with friends on the wing. As they returned to their cell for lockdown, they were approached by three screws, Craig, Williams and another.

"You're being moved to Pentonville," Craig said.

"It's closer to the Old Bailey," Officer Williams said.

"Collect your belongings, the van is waiting," ordered the third officer.

HM Prison Pentonville is commonly known by criminals, cons and prison officers as 'the Ville' and is located on the Caledonian Road in Barnsbury in the London Borough of Islington. The prison was opened in 1842 to house eight hundred and sixty prisoners. It was constructed with a central hall and four radiating wings which were all visible to staff in the centre. Each prison cell was thirteen feet long, seven feet wide and nine feet high with a small window.

The prison van drove across South London, through Kennington, crossed Southwark Bridge and passed Covent Garden. The journey took just over half an hour. The 'Ville' had a reputation for housing hard-core criminals and was governed by the brutality of its screws. Once the brothers were booked in, they were shown to their cell. The following morning, after they'd eaten breakfast, Al and Brian wandered out onto the remand wing.

"I don't believe it," Brian said.

"What?" Al said.

"Over there," Brian said as he pointed. "They have a pool table and... no one is on it."

A smile spread across Al's face.

"Fancy a game?"

"Bloody right," Brian said as he marched over to the chalk board and wrote 'Brian & Al' before racking up the balls.

Al checked the small collection of pool cues and handed Brian one.

"I'll break if you like," Brian said.

"Sure," Al said as he walked around the table.

Brian lined up the cue, closed one eye to take aim and fired the ball down the table sending a red ball into the back of the end pocket.

"You're yellows," Brian said.

Brian walked to the far end of the table, chose a ball and proceeded to line up his cue.

"What are you doing?" a con called out as he came bounding down the wing towards them.

"Take your shot," Al said calmly.

Brian lined up his shot and sent several balls flying around the table.

"Good shot," Al said.

"What do you think you're doing?" the con said as he stopped to catch his breath. "No one plays pool until John is up."

"My shot, isn't it?" Al said as he ignored the con and strolled around the table looking for his opportunity to pot a ball.

"Look you must be either new, mental or have a fucking death wish, because no one plays pool until John is up," the con insisted as he slammed his hand down on the edge of the pool table. "John McQuaid is the guvnor, the daddy, numero uno, number one so you best fuck off before it all gets nasty."

"Who the fuck do you think you're talking to?" Al said as he looked up and faced the con.

The con shook his head in sarcastic awe before walking over to the chalk board and proceeded to rub both Brian's and Al's names off.

Brian walked calmly around the table, picked up the chalk and wrote 'Brian & Al' back on the board before walking back to the table and taking his shot.

The con, looking increasingly agitated, rubbed their names off again.

Brian took his shot and missed the pocket. He placed his cue on the table and strutted back to the board, keeping his eyes fixed on the con and wrote 'Brian & Al' on the chalk board again.

As Brian turned his back, the con raised his hand as if to rub the names off for a third time.

"Touch that board again and I'll fucking do you!" Al said with a glare that made it clear that violence was imminent.

"What's going on here?"

Al and Brian turned to a well-built con who was rubbing the sleep from his eyes, approaching the table.

"I told them, John," the con said in a subservient tone. "Nobody plays until you're up."

Al looked the big fella up and down, tilted his head to the left and then the right before clenching his fists.

"I'm new here and I don't know what all this commotion is about, but I'm telling you this," Al said as his eyes burnt into John McQuaid's. "I don't know who the fuck you are but me and my brother are going to play pool."

From the corner of his eye Al could see that Brian had slipped off his shoe and sock and was filling his sock with pool balls.

John McQuaid stood silent for a moment and then yawned.

"I'm in court on Monday so I don't have any problem," John McQuaid as he stretched his arms.

"Good," Al said with eyes still firmly fixed on John McQuaid's. "I'll see you Monday then."

John turned away and strolled back along the landing to his cell.

Al turned to see the look of utter shock on the con's face.

"I'm sorry lads, I was just following John's orders. I'm Danny," the con said with an awkward smile.

Al looked him up and down and sneered.

"Fuck off you weasel!" Al said before turning back to see Brian putting the pool balls back on the table.

***

Al and Brian served two months at HMP Pentonville, without any major incidents, before being taken to the central criminal court for England and Wales known as the Old Bailey in central London.

Chapter 8

Al and Brian were held in cells below the Old Bailey courthouse.

"How are you doing, Brian?" Al asked.

"What do you think?" Brian said.

Yeah, I suppose so," Al said as he rose to his feet. "Did you hear what that screw was harping on about yesterday?"

"Not really," Brian said as he leaned back against the cell's wall. "I switched off."

"He was telling me about some Nigerian fella called, Kingsley Ibrahim," Al said. "Apparently this guy has raped the wife of some Nigerian big shot and has fled the country."

"Scum," Brian said.

"Well, it turns out that this Nigerian fella, Kingsley, has made his way to England in the hope of evading any kind of retribution from this big shot, but he was wrong. The fella, as you can imagine, is pretty pissed off at what has happened to his wife and has sent the message far and wide to track this Kingsley Ibrahim down," Al said.

"They should cut his bollocks off," Brian said.

"So now Kingsley has been tracked down and nicked in England, and Nigeria has demanded his return, and this is where the screw comes into it," Al said. "Kingsley has been handcuffed to this screw and he is begging and pleading not to be returned but no one is having any of it. The screw has escorted him on the plane all the way to Nigeria where Kingsley and the screw are led by armed officers to the back of a plane hangar. Kingsley has been un-cuffed and positioned, at gun point, against the wall, and then shot dead.

The screw said that he was shitting himself having just witnessed a cold-blooded murder, but they've just led him back into the airport so he could return home."

"Good riddance," Brian said. "Fuck him, he's a rapist. He deserved to die."

"Yeah, but imagine if it wasn't him but someone else and it's a case of mistaken identity," Al said.

"Yeah, but it was him, wasn't it?" Brian asked.

"That's the point. There was no trial, but being taken around the back of a building and shot dead? For all we know the real rapist could still be out there," Al said.

Brian thought about it for a moment.

"So enough of the rapist," Brian said. "What's your gut feeling about how today will go?"

"In my experience of all those working in the system, that's judges, screws, old bill, solicitors, the fucking lot of them, is that there are no feelings about you, me or anyone that finds themselves in front of them," Al said. "The professionals have feelings trained out of them. They become little more than analytical thinkers. They become objective, unfeeling and simply apply the law to the facts that are presented to them."

"So if an old bill fits you up and their version of the facts fits, then you're fucked," Brian said.

"There are scores, maybe even hundreds of victims locked away because of a miscarriage of justice," Al said.

"Bent coppers are even lower than nonces," Brian hissed. "They're playing God with the freedom of others."

"You asked how will today go," Al said. "I'm fucked if I get a guilty on the robbery."

"But you didn't do it," Brian said.

"I know it, you know it, and my barrister believes me, but he reckons that nothing is ever a given and that I should prepare myself for the worst," Al said. "Five years without the robbery and big time if it stands."

The cell door opened, and two screws stepped forward.

"It's time," the larger of the screws said.

Al and Brian were led up the stairs and into the dock enclosure. The judge then had the charges read out. Al was charged with three counts of Actual Bodily Harm (ABH), one count each of Grievous Bodily Harm (GBH), Affray, Criminal Damage and Robbery.

Brian was charged with Affray.

"It wasn't even Brian that battered the landlord's wife," Al thought. *"It was Big Irene."*

"Not guilty," Al replied when asked how he pleaded.

"Not guilty," Brian replied when asked the same question.

The landlord and his wife took the stand and gave their version of events which included Al running up the stairs, armed, forcing the landlord to open the safe and stealing twenty thousand pounds. The defence barrister was quick to point out to the jury that the landlady couldn't remember if the weapon was a gun or a knife. However, they were both confident that it was Al who had committed the robbery despite saying that the robber was wearing a balaclava covering his face.

The prosecution called the amateur wrestler to the stand to give evidence. The defence barrister asked for him to take him through the conversation that led to the alleged offence.

"I heard all the commotion, your Honour, and saw the accused trying to leave the scene," the wrestler said.

"What happened next?" the defence barrister said.

"I grabbed the accused and told him that I was making a citizen's arrest," the wrestler said as he puffed out his chest.

"How did my client respond?"

"He said that he didn't have anything to do with what was happening and was just trying to get away," the wrestler said.

"So what did you do?"

"I believed that he had something to do with the crime and held onto him," the wrestler said.

"What happened next?"

"He was agitated and told me to let him go," the wrestler said. "I told him that I was an amateur wrestler."

"Why did you tell my client that?"

"I wanted to put fear into him so that he remained with me until the police arrived," the wrestler said.

"What happened next?"

"He threatened me," the wrestler said.

"Please, can you tell me exactly what my client was alleged to have said?"

"He said to take my hands off him and that he had nothing to do with what was going on," the wrestler said.

"So my client has now expressed his innocence twice, is that correct?"

"Yes, but I knew he was guilty of something, and I told him that I was not afraid of him," the wrestler said as he turned to address the jury.

"Please, what happened next?"

"He said that this was the final warning and that I had better let him go," the wrestler said.

"Did you let my client go after this third attempt of protesting his innocence?"

"No, I could hear the police sirens and I held him firm," the wrestler said, nodding his head at the jury.

"Please continue," the defence barrister said.

"It was then that he began punching me over and over, one punch after another. I could feel my bones breaking and my teeth breaking in my mouth," the wrestler said. "But I refused to let go of his ankle and I held on until he knocked me unconscious. I think he legged it because when I came around, the police had arrived, and I was rushed to hospital."

"Thank you," the defence barrister said.

"Actually, he kind of did me a favour," the wrestler said. "My teeth were rotten and because he knocked them all out, I got my whole mouth sorted for free."

The judge almost choked, coughed several times and then leaned forward.

"That's all very well but he had no right knocking them out in the first place!" the judge said, shaking his head emphatically.

Al, having witnessed the expression of sheer disbelief on the judge's face, had to stop himself from bursting into fits of laughter.

"Not now… not now," Al thought as he bit his lip.

When the judge summed up the case, he clarified to the jury that three men had run up the stairs wearing balaclavas, there was no evidence of a gun, and that everyone involved in the disturbance was Scottish. The barrister turned and gave Al a half smile.

The jury returned a guilty judgement for the three counts of ABH, the GBH, Affray and Criminal Damage but a not guilty for the robbery.

"Fucking yes!" Al thought as he listened to the outcome.

Al was given a total of seven years to run concurrently. Having already served nine months on remand he had just four and a half months to run.

Brian was found guilty of Affray and with the six months already served, he walked away free.

"We've both had a result here!" Al thought as the screw led him back down to the cells.

Chapter 9

Al was led back to the cells before being taken back to HMP Pentonville along with several other convicted criminals. The compartment inside the sweatbox stunk of piss and shit. Al looked at the phlegm that a prisoner had spat onto the tinted Perspex window.

"Fucking animal," Al thought as he sat back in the chair.

Al felt every bump in the road on the short journey back to the prison. Once inside the reception he went through the same procedure as he had at HMP Brixton and at Pentonville when he first arrived. Only this time Al was a convicted prisoner and not on remand with all the privileges he had prior to the trial.

"Can you count?" the screw said.

Al looked and smiled.

"I can count money."

"Good," the screw said as he filled in his form. "You'll be working in the canteen doing the books. We have systems in place so all you need to do is enter payments received and payments out to suppliers... simple.

Al was handed a set of prison clothes which included a pair of blue jeans, a striped shirt, black shoes, a light blue T-shirt and a blue denim jacket. The screw gave him a new toothbrush and some prison issue toothpaste. He was then led onto a wing for convicted prisoners.

"Al, hello mate," a con said as he walked towards him.

"Eddy," Al said as his eyes lit up when he recognised the con.

"Good to see you mate," Eddy said with a broad grin. "Shame it's not on the outside though."

Al had chatted with Eddy at length just the once while he had been in Brixton. They bonded immediately. Eddy was shipped out the following day to HMP Pentonville as a remand prisoner awaiting trial.

The two men shook hands.

"What did you get?" Al said as he stepped back and looked his friend up and down.

"Yeah, I've lost a few pounds," Eddy said with a grin. "Prison food can do that to a man. I got weighed off for two years but with time already served I've got a little over six months to do. What about you, they had you fitted up on a robbery charge, didn't they?"

"I walked away from that," Al said with an exaggerated sigh. "I've got fourteen weeks and then out."

"Good for you," Eddy said as he patted Al on the shoulder. "It'll be a piece of piss."

"Yeah, right," Al said. "A walk in the park."

Eddy led Al down onto the wing and introduced him to some of the cons. He recognised one face that he'd seen at Brixton. He was a geezer, an armed robber. Al remembered him dripping in gold and his girlfriend wore the shortest of skirts during visiting time.

Al settled in quickly. He wrote to the Director of Prosecutions in Glasgow and admitted his guilt while advising him that he was serving time in HMP Pentonville just as Craig, the screw, had advised him to do while he was in Brixton. When Al shared what he was doing with Eddy, he was shocked and saddened to learn that Craig and his wife were prolific shoplifters. They were caught and found to have a house full of stolen property. Craig had tried desperately to conceal the fact that he was a serving prison officer but when it eventually came out, he committed suicide.

It became apparent very quickly that there were four screws running a scam in the canteen. A one-ounce bag of tobacco was being sold to the inmates at one pound and twenty pence. They had also put twenty per-cent on Mars Bars and the other confectionery. At the end of the month Al had to balance the books and hand them over to the prison officers. He hated doing it and felt physically sick when the screw handed him an ounce of tobacco. Once back on the wing he immediately gave it to his friend, Eddy. Tension was building on the wing when one inmate kicked off:

"Why the fucking hell are we paying one pound twenty for tobacco that we buy in a shop for a quid?" the con said as he slammed his hand down against the wall.

"Just move on!" the screw said.

"I asked you a fucking question," the inmate said as he clenched his fists.

Within seconds three screws had grabbed the inmate and brought him down onto the canteen floor. One screw placed his knee on the inmate's head as they restrained him. Once the inmate stopped struggling, he was heaved up onto his feet and frog-marched out of the canteen.

The following day the inmate was covered in bruises and cuts.

"Fucking bent screws," Al thought as he watched the con join other inmates on the landing. *"Nasty bastards with no scruples."*

Every week one inmate kicked off and complained about the pricing. Each and every one of them was given a vicious beating. The prison doctor backed up the screw confirming that the injuries had all the signs of a prisoner walking into a wall or falling down the stairs.

"I fucking hate this job!" Al thought. *"The only thing that puts a smile on my face is seeing that delivery truck dropping off boxes of Mars Bars... it takes me back to when all this started."*

While being escorted through the prison, the officer stopped and began to do a little dance on a grave. He waved his arms in the air while shuffling his feet.

"See this?" the screw said. "This is Dr Crippen's grave."

Dr Hawley Harvey Crippen was an American Homeopath, ear and eye specialist and medicine dispenser. He was tried and convicted at the Old Bailey in London for the murder of his wife Cora Henrietta Crippen. Dr Crippen was sent to HMP Pentonville where he was executed by John Ellis at 9.00am on Wednesday the 23rd of November 1910.

"No need for that," Al thought as he watched the prison officer jig around on the grave. *"Wanker!"*

***

It always surprised Eddy just how much Al enjoyed the prison macaroni on a Thursday. Every other meal was awful, but he would have double helpings on a Thursday. With just a few weeks before his release, Al was concerned that there would be police officers waiting to arrest him on his release date and take him to Glasgow to face outstanding charges.

"Eddy," Al called out to his friend.

"You look like you've just found a tenner," Eddy said with a chuckle.

"I've had some good news," Al said as he held up a letter.

"What's that then, a love letter from Deborah Harry?" Eddy said.

"Better," Al said with a triumphant smile.

"Better than Blondie?" Eddy said. "Well, this has got to be good."

"It's from the Director of Prosecutions. When I walk out of here... I'm free."

"And rightly so," Al thought. *"Those bastards kicked the shit out of me!"*

Chapter 10

It was just after 8.00am when the gates of HMP Pentonville closed sharply behind him. Al closed his eyes and slowly lifted his head towards the London sky before inhaling deeply.

"Freedom. And it smells damn good," Al thought as he opened his eyes and allowed a broad grin to spread across his face as he looked at the pub opposite. *"A proper pint is just what I need."*

Al stopped on the side of the road and checked for spaces between the rush hour morning traffic. He sped across the road and stopped outside the Caledonian Pub.

"I hope old Bruce is up," Al thought as he knocked on the door enthusiastically.

"Fuck off we're closed!" a voice called.

"Bruce, that's no way to talk to your old mate Al," Al said.

"Al, Al McIntosh! Is that you mate?" Bruce called back while unbolting and unlocking the pub door.

"Who else?" Al said with a chuckle.

The pub door swung open and Al was met with a wild manic grin.

"Al, how the fuck are you?" Bruce said as the two friends shook hands.

Bruce ushered Al in before sticking his head outside and looking up and down the road and closing the door.

"Al, it's good to see you mate," Bruce said as stepped behind the bar and reached for a straight pint glass.

"You too, Bruce," Al said as he pulled out a bar stool.

"So, what's brings you here?" Bruce said as he put the pint of Carlsberg lager on the bar.

"I've just got out," Al said as he reached for the ice-cold lager.

"What, you mean...?" Bruce said as he nodded towards the window.

"Yes mate, and this is a very welcome sight," Al said as he lifted the glass, smiled, and took a sip.

"You mean we've been neighbours all this time and I didn't know," Bruce said, pouring a pint for himself.

"It's not like I could have popped round for a drink," Al said.

Bruce chuckled and then took a long sip of his lager.

"I had heard that you got put away and immediately thought it must have been something to do with Glasgow and you got shipped off back north," Bruce said.

"Nah, it was remand in Brixton and then onto the Ville."

"What was it for?" Bruce asked while he lit a cigarette.

Al told him how he had been picked up in Oxford Street, nicked and then prison time.

"Well mate, it's good to see you free," Bruce said as he raised his glass.

Al drank every last drop before putting the glass on a beer mat.

"Fuck me that tasted good," Al said, as he wiped the froth from his mouth.

"The first one always does," Bruce said as he began to refill the glass.

"So, what's the plan?" Bruce said. "Are you going straight?"

Al laughed out loud.

"What, me get a job and work forty hours for a pittance while reporting to some arsehole of a boss?" Al said as he shook his head. "Not a fucking chance."

"So, are you looking for some proper work?" Bruce said quietly, putting a second pint on the beer mat.

Al shrugged.

"Have you heard of anything?"

"I know of an active team looking for a good wheel man," Bruce said. "Proper people, you'd like them."

Al took a sip of his lager and shook his head.

"I'm not a wheel man, but I appreciate you offering to make an introduction," Al said. "I've not been out an hour yet so there's no rush. Once I've got it sorted in my head, I'll make my moves."

"Are you alright for money?" Bruce asked, reaching into his trouser pocket.

Al nodded.

"Bruce, thanks mate but I'm alright. I pretty much sorted things before I was sent down," Al said as he raised his hand.

"As long as you're sure," Bruce said. "I know you'd do it for me if I was on that side of the bar."

"In a heartbeat Bruce," Al said as the two friends chinked glasses.

Al took two long sips and then put his glass on the bar.

"Bruce, can I use your phone?"

"Yeah, of course you can," Bruce said as he stepped away, opened the bar and motioned Al towards the phone.

"Cheers," Al said as he lifted the telephone receiver and began to dial.

Bruce smiled and stepped away.

Voice: Hello

Al McIntosh: Is that you, Sign On?

Sign On: Yeah, who is this?

Al McIntosh: It's Al McIntosh.

Sign On: Al, hello mate. Great to hear your voice. Where are you?

Al McIntosh: I'm having a drink with Bruce in the Cally opposite the Ville.

Sign On: Fuck me Al, it's not even 9.00!

Al McIntosh: I needed a drink.

Sign On: Al, I've got your bit of scratch all sorted. Can you be at the Earl Russell on the St Pancreas Road for about 10.30am?

Al McIntosh: No problem. I'll be there.

Sign On: See you there.

Al hung up.

Al had reached out to Eddie Robinson while he was awaiting trial. Eddie Robinson was known by all in the criminal world as 'Sign On'. Sign On had three run-down hotels which he would let out. Once a criminal was certain that he would be incarcerated, Sign On would take their National Insurance Number and then use his brother who worked in the labour exchange to register and approve claims. Al had been registered as married with five children. Sign On would claim rent for the room and retain fifty per-cent of the social security payment. Once the criminal had served his time, he would come home to a bundle of cash to help him on his way.

"Thanks Bruce," Al said as he stepped back into the bar area.

"No problem," Bruce said as he stubbed his cigarette out in the ashtray. "Do you want a bit of breakfast? I could rouse the old woman and get her to knock you up some eggs and bacon."

"No, no thanks," Al said before finishing the second pint. "I'm going to get myself off to Kings Cross."

"As long as you're sure," Bruce said.

Al reached into his pocket and produced a small wad of notes.

"Put that away," Bruce said with a smile. "I'm just pleased to see you mate."

Al put the empty glass on the bar and then reached out to shake Bruce's hand.

Bruce raced around the bar and opened the pub door. He stuck his head out before standing aside so that Al could leave.

"Stay lucky," Bruce said.

"You too," Al said before putting both hands into his trouser pockets and striding off.

"Top fella, Bruce," Al thought as he walked towards Piccadilly Tube Station. *"Once I'm all sorted, I'll go back and buy him a few drinks."*

Al bought a ticket and rode the seven-minute journey to King Cross. He stepped out of the train station and looked around him.

"I love this place," Al thought as he rubbed his stomach. *"I'm starving."*

Al turned swiftly on his heels and scampered off to George's Café on York Way near the junction of Wharfdale Road. He looked up briefly at the Pepsi sign and the coloured cardboard star signs offering 'Specials' in the window. He entered and strode up to the counter. Al looked at the menu.

108

"Yes, mate what can I get you?" George, the owner, said.

"Eggs, bacon, sausages, beans and toast, please mate," Al said.

"Do you want two eggs?" George said as scribbled down the order.

"Yeah and I'll have a mug of tea, cheers," Al said.

George grabbed a mug and began to pour from a large stainless steel tea pot. He added a touch of milk and handed Al the piping hot mug of strong tea.

"There's sugar on the table. Breakfast won't be long," George said as he handed the order to his cook.

Al sat by the window and watched as everyday life in the capital passed him by. Just as George put his breakfast on the table, Al's eyes were drawn back to the window. Two beautiful, long-haired blondes strode past wearing black knee-high boots. One girl wore a short black mini dress that rode up with every step while the other wore a flimsy beige mini dress that hugged her every curve.

"Fuck me, I could do with some of that," Al thought before turning back to his hot food.

With a full stomach, Al wandered back towards Kings Cross and the Earl Russell Pub.

The Earl Russell pub had a notorious history dating back to when it was a regular haunt for Charles Darby Sabini, King of the racehorse gangs. The Sabinis dominated the London underworld with extortion, protection and theft in addition to operating several nightclubs. With extensive police and political connections, the hundred-man strong gang protected their empire with imported Sicilian gunmen and horrific razor attacks.

Al entered the pub and immediately spotted Sign On.

"You're looking well," Sign On said as he looked Al up and down. "You boys must love it in there."

"Prefer it out here," Al said as he sat down. "How's business?"

Sign On beamed.

"Thriving Al," Sign On said. "I've got over fifty on my books right now and there's no sign of it letting up."

"You're a shrewd, smart bastard," Al thought as he looked at Sign On dressed in his tailor-made suit. *"You have a cracking scam going on. Good for you!"*

Sign On had a bottle of whiskey on the table and two glasses. He reached out and poured a large one for Al.

"Cheers," Al said.

"There you go," Sign On said as he handed Al a large wad of notes.

"Cheers, that looks like more than I was expecting," Al said before sipping his whiskey.

"I normally take fifty per-cent of the social security payment plus all the rent, but for you, as a mate, I've just kept the rent," Sign On said with a half grin. "You'll find there's eighteen hundred quid."

"Nice one," Al said as his eyes opened wide with surprise. "I appreciate that, Sign On."

"Are you looking for a bit of work?" Sign On said.

"Is it for you?" Al asked.

"No, it'll be with a little kiting firm in Peckham," Sign On said as he poured another whiskey into his glass. "You might know him, Jock Snewen. One of his lads has just been weighed off for GBH. It was a fight in a pub that got out of hand, so there's a spot. I can put in a word if you want."

Cheque kiting is fraud. Individuals or teams travel around using stolen cheque books to buy goods that they later sold on at twenty-five percent of the retail price. The professional kiting crews cash the cheques at banks or have a 'goods wanted' list. Goods are then sold on to the fence, a buyer of stolen property.

"I don't know the fella," Al said as he shook his head. "Thanks, but that's not for me."

Sign On shrugged his shoulders.

"How are you for digs? Have you got a place to stay?" Sign On said as he put a set of keys on the table.

"I have now," Al said as he reached over for the keys. "Thanks for that, you're a diamond."

Chapter 11

Al lay back on the standard size double bed. He had felt and sniffed the sheets and was pleased that they were clean. It was a single, basic, room where the original wallpaper had been painted over in chocolate brown and contrasting beige. There was a small wooden table, two chairs and a sink.

He put his hands behind his head and allowed his mind to drift; an image of his Da came up.

"What a completely useless waste of space you were Da," Al thought. *"You never worked a day in your life despite having nine children. What a selfish man you were."*

An image of the Four Crowns tattoo his Da had on his knuckles shot into his mind.

"Wine, Four Crown wine and the pub was your life," Al thought. *"A low life alcoholic devoid of any moral responsibility."*

Al found himself slowly shaking his head as an image of Mammy then came up.

"Evil. A fucking degenerate psychopathic sadist," Al thought, gritting his teeth. *"What kind of a mother takes her frustrations out on her innocent kids? The violence you inflicted on Beth and Wullie was unforgiveable!"*

Al could picture his young sister being grabbed by the hair and dragged screaming into the front room where she was stripped naked and beaten with a dog chain.

"My brother Wullie, you depraved bitch," Al thought as he shifted uncomfortably on the bed. *"I had to carry him miles to hospital after you hammered a sewing needle into his knee. We were both*

so scared to tell the doctor the truth, we made up shit about how Wullie must have fallen on it while playing football."

An image of his mammy with one clenched fist raised and a metal horseshoe in her other hand came to mind. Her immoral smile hid the wickedness she was capable of.

"I fucking hate you and fucking hate what you did to us all," Al thought as he balled his hand into a tight fist.

Al was visualising himself being forced to strip naked and put on a dress before the front door was opened and Mammy threw him out onto the street where his friends and neighbours were playing, yelling out at the top of her voice 'You'll never be a poof!'.

Al forced the image from his head. He sighed heavily and relaxed his tightly clenched fists.

"Wullie, you poor bastard," Al thought as he visualised Wullie sitting on the roof and looking up at the rising sun after they had been out leading for night.

Al pictured Wullie telling him how he regularly spoke to Jesus and that he had told him to kill Mammy.

"I hope that you're finding peace out there on the moors as a gamekeeper," Al thought. *"Right, enough of all that. Now, what am I going to do? A day job is out of the question, so what about going back to the 'smash and grab'? There are hundreds of jewellery shops around London, I can place everything I steal, and the money is pretty good."*

Al shifted from lying on his back to his right side.

"I've been there and done that," Al thought. *"I can do better than that and I am destined to become more. I can feel it in my bones. Bank robberies.... What if I move up to robbing banks? I've met some absolute fucking clowns who have robbed banks so I know I can do better than them. How fucking hard can it be? Scope the place out and get some inside information if possible. Then its*

shooters, masks, gloves and storm the place, crowd control and steal the cash. In and out of the bank in minutes, then a good wheel man, ideally with motor racing experience and we're gone. Divide up the cash with my lads and then party hard."

An image of a 'have a go' security guard hero entered his mind.

"Don't you dare stand between me and the money!" Al thought as he imagined himself lowering a sawn-off shotgun and blasting the security guard in the leg.

Al sat bolt upright.

"I can't sit around here thinking about bollocks all day," Al thought as he stood up and checked his reflection in the mirror.

Al left the bedsit and took the underground to Finsbury Park. He strolled down Gloucester Drive and then stopped briefly to look at the squat where he stayed with Gas Man, Eddy, Black Willey the armed robber, and the lovely Delores.

"We had some good times," Al thought as he turned and carried on walking past three more houses. "I hope she's in."

Al walked up the pathway and then knocked on the large wooden six panel front door. The door opened. In front of him stood a woman with ringlets of tawny brown hair that curtained her oval face. Her eyes were a vivacious brown and her cupid's bow lips were succulent, sultry and velvet soft.

"Hello Madge," Al said with an enthusiastic grin.

Madge was the brothel's Madam.

"Well, I never! Come in, come in," Madge said as she opened the door further and beckoned him in.

Once inside Madge took a small step and looked Al up and down.

"Come here," Madge said as she flung her arms around him and squeezed tight. "I thought we'd seen the last of you. Come on through."

Al followed Madge down the hallway. He glanced up to his left and spotted two scantily clad girls giggling at the top of the stairs. Once inside the kitchen Madge motioned for him to sit at the table.

"What would you like? Tea, coffee or something stronger?" Madge said as she opened the cupboard and produced a bottle of Johnnie Walker Whiskey.

"I'll have a whiskey with you Madge," Al said, still grinning.

"Are you back for good?" Madge said as she placed an empty glass tumbler in front of him.

"You know me and London," Al said as he watched Madge pour the whiskey.

"I heard you got sent down," Madge said as she screwed the cap back on the bottle and sat down. "Cheers."

"Cheers," Al said as they clinked glasses. "It could have been worse, Madge, much worse. The bastards did everything to try and fit me up."

"Corrupt, the lot of them," Madge hissed. "I've heard of girls being picked up and told it's a blow job or the slammer. Some of those at the top are the greatest villains never to have been hung."

"Are you having problems with the old bill here?"

Madge shook her head.

"No, we keep quite a low profile. We have our regulars, and they bring friends who bring friends of friends. It's not like the girls standing on street corners," Madge said. "I still have a few of the girls who were here when you lived in the squat opposite, but most come and go. I've seen a rise in girls from all over in recent months.

115

I've got a girl from Hull, another from Carlisle, and one just arrived yesterday from Belfast."

"So business is still good?"

Madge nodded before taking a sip of her drink.

"Some men are driven by a compulsive desire for sex. They want it fresh, exciting and new. On Monday a punter will want a blonde and then that same punter will only have a redhead on the Wednesday and a brunette on Friday. I have some that come here, busy city professionals, who have no time or desire to develop real relationships. They need to skip past the first three dates and get straight down to what they want. It takes all sorts, and my girls will try their best to fulfil all their desires," Madge said as she took a big gulp. "Are you looking for a date?"

Al shook his head.

"I have this one girl; the regulars call her 'Blow Job' because... well, she can do this thing with her tongue that just keeps those men coming back," Madge said with a chuckle.

"No, I was hoping to find Mae West," Al said.

"She's moved sweetheart," Madge said as she topped up Al's glass.

"Do you have an address or a phone number?" Al asked.

Madge shook her head.

"Wait a minute... Mae did give me a number, but I can't for the life of me remember where I put it," said Madge. "If it comes back to me, I'll find you. Are you staying on the manor?"

"I've got a temporary place, but I need to be around here, really," Al said.

"Well, the place across the road is empty and ripe for a squat," Madge said as she hunched her shoulders. "Anyway, where is that handsome brother of yours, Brian?"

Al began to chuckle.

"I've heard my brother called a lot of things in my time but never handsome," Al said.

"There were a couple of girls here that were quite sweet on him," Madge said.

"Brian and I were banged up together in Brixton on remand, and then Pentonville before sentencing. Brian walked away having already served time and I had to finish mine. I think he's gone back to Glasgow."

"He'll be back," Madge said with a wry smile. "Once he knows you're out and that inevitable pull to London kicks in... oh yes, he'll back."

Al drank the last of his whiskey and put the empty glass down.

"It's been good catching up Madge," Al said as he stood up. "I'm going to check out the place opposite. I'd really appreciate it if you could have a look for Mae's telephone number."

"Leave it with me," Madge said as she rose from the table and led Al back through the hallway.

Al glanced to his right. His eyes were met by a tall blonde girl wearing white stockings, suspenders and a cream-coloured dressing gown. She pouted her lips and blew him a kiss.

"Not just yet," Al thought as he smiled and turned away. *"You've got to get yourself sorted."*

"Don't be a stranger," Madge said as she leaned forward and kissed his cheek.

Al winked, smiled and then looked over at the house opposite.

"Madge is right," Al thought as he looked at the windows. *"There's no curtains. What a result!"*

A silver Rover P5B stopped directly outside the house. Al watched as the man inside removed his tie and undid his top button before checking his reflection in the rear-view mirror. Al smiled to himself as the man got out and locked his car.

"That could be the first of many punters for Madge today," Al thought as he turned back and crossed the road.

Al looked through the front window.

"It's empty alright," Al thought.

Al tried the handle on the wooden back gate. It opened.

"Sweet!" Al thought.

He walked down the side of the semi-detached house and stopped by the back door. He swivelled the handle back and forth.

"It's locked," Al thought as he turned to his right and then shoved his shoulder hard into the side of the door where the lock was.

Bang!

The door swung open. Al stepped inside and closed the door behind him.

"This is it. A place to call home for a while," Al thought as he wandered from one to room to another.

Within a few hours Al had turned the electricity and water back on, bought and fitted a new front door and back door lock. He returned the bedsit keys to Sign On and managed to talk him into selling him a bed, bedding and some furniture for the front room.

Chapter 12

Al was cleaning his teeth when *'Substitute'* by Clout began to play from the portable Motorola transistor radio he'd bought in the pub the day before. He stopped brushing and reached over to turn up the volume.

"I'll be your substitute, whenever you need me," Al hummed as he brushed his teeth.

As he washed out the brush and placed it on the shelf his attention was drawn to the robust throaty growl of a British motorcycle.

"What the hell is that?" Al thought as he bounded down the stairs and into the living room.

Al stepped back a little from the window and then peered around it. Outside he spotted a glossy black British bike parked outside Madge's brothel opposite. As he scanned further, he saw two people, a man and woman standing outside Madge's front door.

"I suppose it takes all sorts," Al thought as he watched the front door open, an exchange of words and then Madge pointed to his house."

"Is that…? It can't be…! Yes, it's Brian!" Al thought.

Al raced back upstairs and put on a shirt before racing back down the stairs just in time to open the front door.

"Brian! Good to see you!" Al said as the two brothers shook hands.

"Al, this is Sandy," Brian said.

Sandy stood a little over five foot six inches. Her swirls of mousey blonde hair garlanded her angular shaped face. Sandy had a saffron tint to her complexion and a warm, friendly, smile. She wore blue

Levi jeans, black biker boots and a heavy black studded leather biker jacket. Al thought Sandy looked every bit the rebellious biker.

"Hi Sandy, nice bike. It's a very nice bike," Al said as he looked over her shoulder.

Sandy smiled and turned to face the bike which was resting on its side stand.

"It would be hard to find another quite like it," Sandy said proudly.

"What is it... a Triumph?" Al said as he took several steps down the pathway.

"It's a Triton." Sandy said as she stood by his side.

"I've never heard of Triton," Al said as he looked the bike up and down. "Is it British?"

"It's one hundred percent British and totally custom made to look good and perform out on the streets," Sandy said. "The engine is a powerful 600cc Triumph twin, and it was slotted into a Norton featherbed frame. This combination gave my bike the best of worlds; a reliable engine that can do a ton out on the road and a lightweight frame to make it handle."

"Impressive," said Al.

"So what, are we going to talk about bikes all day or go and have a drink?" Brian said. "We've been on the road for nearly twelve hours."

"Fuck me, you must both be gasping," Al said with a chuckle.

"Gasping!" Brian said, as he rearranged his trousers. "I'm a bit saddle sore too."

Al bolted back inside and grabbed his wallet.

"We'll go to the 'Russell'." Al said as he turned to walk down Gloucester Drive.

"Fuck that walking game," Brian said. "We'll go on the bike."

Al turned and looked at the Triton.

"What, all three of us?"

"Why not," Sandy said with a chuckle. "It wouldn't be the first time."

"We don't have enough helmets," Al said.

"So?" Sandy said as she kicked the Triton over.

The bike roared into life.

Reluctantly Al climbed onto the back of the motorcycle. Sandy held in the clutch and crunched the foot shifter into first gear. With a glance over her shoulder, she blipped the throttle a couple of times before pulling out into the drive. The Triton thundered down the road with Al barking out directions over the loud roar of the motorcycle. Sandy came to a halt outside the Earl of Russell pub.

Brian and Sandy found an empty table while Al went to the bar and ordered a round of lagers with whiskey chasers.

Al was thrilled to see his brother, Brian, and his girlfriend, Sandy, was intriguing. Over two drinks Al learnt that she had a deep sense of adventure and a primal love for British motorcycles. From the stories she shared, Al gleaned that Sandy possessed an unfaltering loyalty to the biker subculture and to the man in her life. He was happy for Brian.

"Are you here to stay?" Al asked as he reached for his third pint.

Brian glanced over at Sandy and then back to Al.

"Yeah, we'll definitely be here for a while," Brian said as he lit a match and held it up for Sandy to light her cigarette.

"Have you got anything lined up yet?" Brian said, lowering his voice.

"I'm thinking smash and grab or banks," Al replied matter of factly.

Brian reached into his pocket and pulled out a folded envelope.

"There you go, Al," Brian said as he handed over the envelope. "Put that in your pocket."

Al peeled the envelope open. It was stuffed with five- and ten-pound notes.

"What's this for?" Al asked, still looking down at the envelope.

"It's a bit of walking around money until you get yourself sorted."

"Are you sure?"

"You'd do it for me, wouldn't you?" Brian said.

"In a heartbeat," Al said as he smiled and pushed the envelope into his trouser pocket. "Thanks Brian. Listen, why don't you come into the smash and grab with me? Its good money and I can place everything we get."

Brian hesitated for a moment and then looked over at Sandy. She smiled and nodded.

"We have our own thing going on," Brian said. "Well, when I say we, I mean this was Sandy's bit of business and she cut me in. Go on Sandy, you tell him."

"Are you familiar with registered mail?" Sandy said.

Al nodded.

"That's what you use when you want to send money, right?"

"That's right, and they use a special envelope that lets the post office know that they are handling registered mail," Sandy said with a wry grin. "It's also tells me exactly where the money is."

"So what, are you doing post offices?"

Sandy shook her head.

"We intercept the mailbags when they arrive at train stations," Sandy said.

"No shooters, no violence, we just walk in and then walk out," Brian said.

"Is it good money?" Al said as he reached over the table for his whiskey chaser.

Brian beamed.

"We make between three and five thousand pounds a week," Brian said.

"Fuck me!" Al muttered under his breath.

"This girl is smart... very smart," Al thought.

"We'll have a wander down to Kings Cross tomorrow, but everything tells us that it'll be no different to Glasgow," Brian said.

"I'm pleased for both of you. You're smart, very smart," Al said as he swallowed the last of his whiskey chaser.

"Come in with us," Sandy said.

"What?" Al said.

"You heard her, Al. Come in with us," Brian said.

"It's a bigger station so more money to go around," Sandy said.

"I think this calls for another round of drinks," Al said as he rose from the table.

As he strolled over to the bar he heard *'Kiss You All Over'* by Exile playing on the jukebox.

"This is bloody good of Brian and Sandy but I'm going to keep my options open. Banks are big money and that's what I want," Al

thought as he handed over a ten-pound note for the round of drinks.

Sandy confessed that she would like to ride around Europe, maybe even the world on her Triton. Brian made a joke that he would need his own bike and would need to stop every three or four hours.

Just as *'Wuthering Heights'* by Kate Bush began to play, the pub door opened. It was Madge, the Madam from the brothel.

"I told him it wouldn't be long before you'd be here," Madge said as she joined them.

"Whiskey?" Al said as he stood up.

"Yes, please sweetheart and can you make it a double?" Madge said.

"I fucking love London," Al thought as he ordered another round of drinks. *"And it's about to get a whole lot better."*

"I've got something for you," Madge said as she handed Al a folded piece of paper.

Al unfolded it.

"Now there is one happy man," Madge said, pointing out Al's upturned lip and a face that reflected genuine happiness.

Madge stayed for two more drinks before returning to her brothel in Gloucester Drive. Al, Brian and Sandy celebrated being together until gone midnight.

"Are you alright to ride, Sandy?" Al said as he staggered over to the Triton.

"Yeah, of course," she slurred.

"So what is it, back to your place?" Brian said.

"We're in London!" Sandy yelled. "So let's go and see some of it!"

Brian burst out laughing at Sandy's excitement.

Sandy climbed onto the motorcycle and put the key in the ignition. She kicked it over and once again it burst into life with a thunderous growl.

"I ain't wearing a helmet," Sandy declared. "I hate wearing crash hats."

"I don't like them either," Brian slurred before clambering onto the back of the bike.

"Well I ain't got one to hate," Al said as he mounted the bike.

Sandy and Brian burst into fits of drunken laughter.

With the headlights turned on, Sandy revved the engine, dropped the clutch and roared down the road. Al could feel the fresh air pounding his face as Sandy accelerated though the gears. As they rode down the Marylebone Road, Al spotted a uniformed police officer.

"Slow down and pull over," Al yelled out as he tapped Sandy on the shoulder.

Sandy came to a complete halt next to the police officer.

"Excuse me," Al called.

The police officer stopped walking and turned to see the three of them sitting on the motorcycle without crash helmets. The officer strutted towards them."

"I'd like you to turn the engine off madam," the officer said.

Al's arm shot out and knocked the police officer's helmet clean off his head.

"Go, go, go!" Al yelled with a raucous laugh.

The three friends roared off into the night laughing.

—

Chapter 13

The following day Al, Brian and Sandy strolled down to Kings Cross train station. Sandy led them out onto the platform to where the night train had brought in the mail. There was no one there.

"Just like Glasgow," Sandy whispered.

"Right then, tomorrow we go to work," Brian said. "In the meantime, I could do with a drink."

"Let's go and have a couple in the Happy Man pub in Finsbury Park," Al said. "I need to make a phone call."

Brian bought three underground tickets to Finsbury Park. The journey took just over four minutes. Once inside the Happy Man pub, Al used the public phone. He dialled the number, the line connected, and Al pushed his coin into the slot.

Al: Hello, is that you Mae?

Voice: No, this is Joe, his boyfriend. Who is this?

Al: Hello Joe. I'm Al, Al McIntosh, a friend of Mae's.

Joe: Al, I have heard so much about you. Mae is always talking about you. He'll be so happy that you've called. Where are you?

Al: I've just taken a place in Gloucester Drive. It's right opposite Madge's place. Mae will know it.

Joe: Mae will be back later today. I'll let him know that you've called and where you are.

Al: I appreciate that, Joe. You take care.

Joe: You too Al.

Al hung up the phone.

Brian had been to the bar and brought over a tray of drinks.

"Did you get to speak with Mae?"

"No but his boyfriend Joe will pass on the address," Al said.

"It'll be good to see Mae again," Brian said before taking a sip of his lager.

"It'll be fucking great!" Al thought as he reached over for his pint.

"Hello Al."

Al looked up to see an unfamiliar face.

"It's Vinnie, mate."

"Who the fuck are you?" Al thought.

"I'm a mate of Gas Man. I met you at the squat a few years back," Vinnie said as he pulled out a chair.

"Oh right, of course. How are you? Have you seen Gas Man?" Al said.

"I don't know who the fuck you are, mate," Al thought.

Vinnie put his pint on the table and sat down.

"I haven't seen Gas Man in a while. The last I heard he got nicked, bailed and then did a runner," Vinnie said with a forced laugh.

Al introduced Vinnie to Brian and Sandy.

"I was in here last night," Vinnie said, rolling his eyes. "Put my foot right in it."

"Why, what did you do?" Sandy said.

"I got chatting with this bird that worked in the local newspaper shop. Sweet little thing called Gwen," Vinnie said.

"Nice name," Sandy said with a grin.

"I would buy my Sun newspaper and we would start chatting and it seemed like we had a lot in common. After a week or so I'd walk in, and she'd smile and say 'Hello Vinnie'. It was then that I thought I just had to roll the dice," Vinnie said.

"You mean you wanted to ask her out?" Sandy said.

"You've got it. So, I waited another week just to be sure and then I've just come out with it," Vinnie said.

"Where did you take her... somewhere nice?" Sandy said, winking slyly at Brian.

"Well, it being the first kind of date I thought we'd just come in here and have a couple of drinks and you know, just kinda get to know each other better," Vinnie said with an exaggerated sigh.

"Sounds sensible," Brian said gently nudging Sandy.

"Well, I've turned up in my best gear, strolled in and she was already here so I've gone up to her and asked what she wanted to drink," Vinnie said. "Once I brought her gin and tonic back to the table, she just clammed up. It didn't matter what I asked or said she would just shrug her shoulders or nod. I wasn't sure if it was nerves, anxiety or that she was just disappointed."

"Oh, I'm sure it wouldn't have been disappointment," Sandy said with a wry grin.

"I would have made my excuses and fucked off," Al thought.

"Well, the thought did cross my mind," Vinnie said. "Then out of nowhere she just asked why I was asking her so many questions. She seemed to be annoyed with me. I tried to laugh it off with a few jokes but that seemed to aggravate her more."

"It's not sounding good," Al said.

"I could feel it all slipping away," Vinnie said. "Anyway, this record has come on the jukebox *'Boogie Oogie Oogie'* by A Taste of Honey and she seemed to perk up, so I suggested a game of pool at the back.

"Seems like a sensible idea if she's not talking," Sandy said. "At least you can still pot a few balls together."

"Well, that table," Vinnie said pointing to the pool table at the back of the bar, "is coin operated, so I put the coins in the slot and pushed it into the table to release the balls. Well, it must have been at an awkward angle because one of the coins shot out. So, I've got down on my hands and knees to fish around for the coin and there in front of me is a gold ring. I've thought 'what a result, someone must have lost it'. Anyway, with the ring in my hand and me down on my knees, I'm now looking up at Gwen."

Al looked over at Sandy biting her lip.

"I'm not kidding when I say there was a look of absolute panic on her face. It dawned on me what this must look like, and I've tried blurting out some kind of an explanation while she's slowly edging away from the pool table. Then as I've stood up, she's just turned and bolted for the door."

"She didn't feel like getting married then," Sandy said, still biting her lip.

"No, I wasn't proposing," Vinnie said with a straight face.

"It's going to be difficult going back to the newspaper shop for your copy of The Sun," Brian said.

"Tell me about it," Vinnie said with a heavy sigh. "I walked past the shop three times this morning to see if she was in there."

"Was she?" Al asked.

"I don't know," Vinnie said. "I ended up walking over a mile to another shop. The thing is, I don't want to have to do that every day. Do you think I should go in and try to explain myself again?"

"If I was you," Sandy said as she wiped a single tear from her eye. "I would just go in and buy your newspaper and say absolutely nothing."

"Yeah," Vinnie said before drinking the last of his lager. "I'm going to do that first thing in the morning."

"Good for you," Brian said.

"Anyway, good to see you Al, and nice to meet you Brian and Sandy," Vinnie said as he rose from the table. "Maybe I'll catch you later."

"Not if I see you first," Al thought.

Vinnie raised his hand at a group of lads further down the bar.

"What a snoozer," Brian said. "How the hell do you know him?"

"I don't," Al said, shrugging his shoulders. "I can honestly say that I have absolutely no recollection of him at all."

Both Sandy and Brian began to laugh.

"Definitely a yawner," Sandy said. "Maybe he sent you to sleep."

"He damn near did it again then," Al said bluntly.

Brian choked on his lager before laughing out loud.

It was just after 8.00 pm when Al, Brian and Sandy were walking up Gloucester Drive when they heard a loud scream and spotted a girl in just her black panties run out of Madge's brothel and down the road towards them.

"What the fuck is going on here?" Al thought as he stepped out onto the road.

131

A large, overweight, man dressed in just his underpants and a white shirt was racing down the road behind her.

"Come here darling," Al said calmly as he motioned the girl to get behind him.

The half-dressed punter was red-faced and clearly angry.

"Alright then mate, what's going on?" Al said, holding up his right hand.

"He wanted to do it without a rubber," the girl said in a broad Irish accent. "When I told him no, he got angry."

The half-naked man was huffing and puffing and then made a sudden lunge for the girl.

"Alright," Al said firmly. "You have to behave yourself my friend. The girl has said no to sex without a condom and rightly so. It's important to protect yourselves, now come on, go get your clothes and get yourself home."

"Don't you know who I fucking am?" the punter hissed through gritted teeth.

"How many times have I heard that," Al thought as he took two steps closer to the angry punter.

"I don't give a monkey's toss who you are mate and trust me you really don't want some of me. I promise it'll make your day considerably worse," Al said with a hint of imminent violence in his voice.

"Well, she should have said right from the off," the punter said.

"I did, I did," the girl said as she slipped her arms through Sandy's leather biker jacket. "I told him protected sex only."

"Lying bitch," the punter said.

"I'm not going to tell you again," Al said as he clenched his fists and took a single step closer.

The punter looked into Al's face before turning swiftly and stomping off back up the road. Al and Brian stopped outside the squat, while Sandy walked the girl back to Madge's brothel. From the corner of his eye Al noticed a white transit van. The doors opened and two men with Mediterranean complexions approached them. The larger of the two men stopped directly in front of Al. He looked him up and down and shook his head slowly.

"Why are you giving my mate hassle?"

"Listen lads we're not looking for any trouble, alright," Al said with a friendly grin. "Your friend wanted sex without a condom and the girl said no, so that means no."

"What has that got to do with you?"

"The girl needed help and your mate didn't look like he was ready to have any kind of sensible conversation," Al said.

"Well. you're fucked now, because I'm the hardest man in Greece," the larger man said, pointing his finger at Al.

"Yeah," said the hardest man in Greece's friend, "and I'm the second hardest!"

Brian stepped forward and stood by his brother.

"See him," Brian said as he pointed to Al, "he's the hardest man in Scotland and me... well, I'm the second hardest."

Brian pulled out a sawn-off pool cue from his inside jacket pocket and lunged forward with an almighty swing that caught his target around the head.

Al could feel an instant surge of adrenaline race through his body. Greece's number one threw a clumsy punch that soared past Al's head. With his guard wide open Al launched a series of vicious

133

hooks, left, right and then left again. The Greek stumbled back when Al took aim and fired his foot straight between the Greeks legs. He yelled out and buckled over as Al's shoe found its target.

"Argh... argh..." the second Greek yelled as Brian held him around the throat and battered his face over and over with the sawn-off pool cue.

Al grabbed the Greek by the hair with both hands, yelled out, and brought his face down hard onto his knee.

CRACK!

Al released his hair, stepped back, found his spot and hurled a left hook, quickly followed by an almighty right uppercut that sent the Greek sprawling onto the road. Al then strode over to the metal dustbin on the roadside and took the lid off. He marched back and looked down on his adversary. His face was covered in blood; his nose was broken, and his body was limp. Al shook his head before reaching down and grabbing his shirt.

SMACK! SMACK! SMACK!

Al battered the Greek with the dustbin lid. He was beaten.

Al looked over at his brother Brian. Greek number two was lying on the floor with Brian sitting on his chest. With both hands he raised the sawn-off cue and then drove it deep into his victim's shoulder.

"Arghh!" the second Greek cried out.

"Are you alright Brian?" Al said as he stood victorious.

"A pair of chancers," Brian said calmly.

"Come on," Al said as he reached out his hand to the beaten Greek. "It's time for you boys to be on your way."

Al helped him to his feet and then over to the white van. Brian had done the same and was pushing his bloody, beaten victim into the passenger side of the Transit van.

"Number 52," the Greek whimpered as Al slammed the driver's door shut.

"This ain't over," Al thought. *"This fella has clocked the door number and he'll be back."*

Chapter 14

All Al's instincts cried out that the altercation with the Greeks was far from over. With Brian's help, they moved clothes, furniture and some personal effects over to an empty house two doors down from Madge's brothel. The following morning Brian and Sandy travelled down to Kings Cross Station. Within just a few minutes they had entered the station and helped themselves to a bag of registered mail and walked out without anyone noticing.

"This is easy money," Al thought as he watched his brother and Sandy empty the sack onto the floor and open the envelopes.

The first envelope that Brian opened had eighty-six pounds in it. He put it in piles of denominations on the teak coffee table. Sandy beamed as her envelope revealed one hundred pounds in five-pound notes. Both Al and Sandy burst out laughing as Brian ripped another envelope revealing just four pounds. Envelope after envelope added to the stacks of cash on the table. Brian handed the final envelope for Sandy to open. She grinned, turned the envelope over several times and with a glint in her eyes, she tore it open.

"Sixty-seven pounds," Sandy said as she placed the final wad of notes on the table. "That makes three thousand six hundred and sixty-three pounds exactly."

"Nice," Brian said.

"Bloody magic!" Al thought.

Sandy separated the cash into three piles and then handed Al and Brian one thousand two hundred and twenty-one pounds each.

Al folded the wad of notes and wedged it into his trouser pocket.

"Thank you," Al said as he patted his pocket.

"You earned it," Brian said with a laugh.

"I'm going to take a look around London," Sandy said as she reached for her crash helmet. "It'll give you guys a chance to catch up."

"Alright Sandy, I'll see you later. Maybe we'll go and have some fish and chips or something," Brian said.

"You certainly know how to charm a girl," Sandy said as she slipped her crash helmet on and opened the front door. "Maybe I'll have the something."

"She is one smart cookie," Al said after the front door closed.

"She certainly is," Brian said as he sat back on the armchair. "She'd been nicking the registered mail for a while before we met."

"Do you know how she came across the opportunity?" Al asked as he looked out of the window to number 52 opposite.

"Sandy said that she had arrived back from somewhere on the train and saw the piles of post of the platform. One of the bags was open and she saw the registered mail, so she just reached in and took a handful and carried on walking. Once she was home, she opened the envelopes and found she was six hundred and forty pounds richer."

"Money like that would explain the custom-built motorcycle," Al said.

"She loves motorcycles and the open road," Brian said as he leant forward. "We've ridden all over Scotland together and when I told her about my brother and London she just said, 'Let's go'."

"It sounds like you have found yourself a diamond," Al said with a smile.

"One day at a time," Brian said.

KNOCK! KNOCK!

Al shot up out of the chair and bolted over to the window and then let out a sigh of relief when he saw Madge. He turned back to see Brian standing with his legs apart holding the sawn-off pool cue.

"It's alright," Al said as he motioned Brian to put the weapon away.

Al opened the front door.

"Hello Madge, come in," Al said as he beckoned her into the front room.

"My girls told me what you did last night," Madge said as she put her hands on her hips. "They were impressed by how you diffused the angry punter wanting to dip his dick without a rubber and then took care of business with his two mates."

"It's not a problem, happy to help," Al said.

"It could have got a lot worse, and I don't want any of my girls in harm's way," Madge said as she looked Al up and down and then turned her gaze to Brian. "We don't get a lot of trouble but if it happens, I need it sorted out quickly so we can get back down to business. So... how about looking after my brothel, Al? I'll give you five hundred quid a week plus there will be benefits."

Madge chuckled.

"Fuck me," Al thought as he stroked his chin. *"One minute I'm thinking about what I'm going to do and the next minute my brother Brian has pulled me into his bit of business which could mean a couple of thousand a week, and now Madge is offering up five hundred quid."*

"I have to be honest," Al said as he faced Madge. "It's not really my bag."

"I'm looking for something big, really big and something challenging that will be all mine," Al thought.

"If I'm here and it kicks off at your place Madge, I'll be in like a shot," Al said. "That goes without saying, but I can't go on your books."

"That's a shame," Madge said.

"Look, I do know someone that could help though," Al said.

"Is he good?" Madge said as she pounded her fist into her open palm.

Al chuckled.

"Trust me the fella I've got in mind will give you everything and more," Al said with a smile. "Plus, you don't have to pay him five hundred pounds… That's too much. My fella will do it for three hundred… okay?"

"If you recommend him then that's good enough for me," Madge said.

"I'll see him later when we go down to the Bell in Kings Cross for a few drinks and I'll keep you posted," Al said.

Madge grinned.

"It's good seeing you two together."

Madge looked down at her watch.

"I've gotta go," Madge said, and turned and walked back to the front door. "We have a couple of regulars due anytime."

Al and Brian sat back in their armchairs.

"Brian what's with the sawn-off pool cue?" Al asked.

Brian hesitated for a moment.

"Protection," Brian said as he put both hands palm down on the armchair rests.

"Really?" Al said with a quizzical expression. "You're more than capable of taking care of most business with your fists."

Brian hesitated again.

"It's Wullie," Brian said.

"Wullie, you mean brother Wullie?" Al said, shaking his head.

"You don't know the half of it," Brian said.

"Half of what?" Al asked.

"Wullie came back from that gamekeeper's job tooled up with a shotgun and a fucking great cattle prod," Brian said.

"A cattle prod?" Al said.

"Yeah, you know the electric stick they use to move cattle and livestock about," Brian said. "I'm not kidding you; I saw him prod this fella in the pub because he spilt his beer. There was this fucking great crackle, and this fella is on the floor wriggling around with his tongue hanging out and only the whites of his eyes on show."

"That doesn't sound good," Al said.

"That wasn't the first time either," Brian said. "I'm telling you Al; our brother has fucking gone mate. If he told me he was going to kill mammy once, then he told me a hundred times and that look in his eyes told me that I needed to be ready if he suddenly turned on me."

"I knew he wasn't right," Al said. "But I thought it would pass with time."

Brian shook his head.

"There is more."

"I think you better tell me the rest," Al said.

Brian took a deep breath.

140

"He was torturing Glen," Brian said.

"What Glen... our dog Glen?" Al said almost in disbelief.

Glen was the family pet and Al loved his dog.

"I saw it with my own eyes," Brian said. "I've seen him ram a hot poker straight up the dog's arse."

Al could feel his stomach tighten as the words left Brian's lips.

"When we were out he would tie Glen up, hang him by his back legs on the washing line and then do all sorts of nasty shit," Brian said.

Al clenched, released and clenched his fists over and over.

"That night when we were coming home and you called out.... Remember?"

Al nodded.

"That was when Glen jumped out of the window," Al said.

Brian shook his head.

"When I walked through the door with Wullie, Glen scrambled to his feet and just bolted towards the closed window," Brian said. "It wasn't your voice that caused Glen to jump out of the window. The dog was shit scared of Wullie."

Al could feel himself gritting his teeth. Anger was building in his stomach as he clenched his fists tighter.

"Wullie will fucking pay for what he did to my dog," Al hissed. "That bastard will fucking suffer. You should have told me Brian."

"How could I, Al?" Brian pleaded. "I knew what you would do to him and despite everything I still feel sorry for him. He's been fucked up Al, fucked up my that evil bitch of a mammy."

"I want to fucking hurt you Wullie, but I know what she did to you and Beth," Al thought as he slowly released his fists.

"I need you to give me your word, Al, that you won't say anything to Wullie," Brian said.

"Glen was my fucking dog!" Al yelled

"I know, Al, but Wullie isn't right in the head," Brian said. "That's why I'm carrying this sawn-off pool cue."

Al hesitated for a moment, took a deep breath and slowly exhaled.

"I give you my word," Al said reluctantly.

The screeching of tyres outside caused Al to rise sharply to his feet. He walked gingerly towards the window. On the opposite side of the road, a large double wheelbase transit van had come to an abrupt halt. Brian joined his brother on the opposite side of the window.

"I fucking knew they would be back," Al whispered.

"You did say." Brian said as he reached for his sawn-off pool cue. "What do you want to do?"

The brothers watched as the van's driver opened the rear doors and eight men stepped out carrying pickaxe handles, tyre levers and bicycle chains. The final man to step out of the van carried a shotgun. It was the guy carrying the shooter that led the men up the pathway and kicked open the front door. Al and Brian watched as the men raced through the door brandishing their weapons.

"I knew it, I bloody well knew it!" Al thought. *"I must always trust my instincts!"*

BANG!

BANG!

Instinctively Al and Brian crouched down for cover when they heard the sound of gun fire.

Al and Brian slowly rose up and peeked out from behind the curtains. One by one the men left the house and clambered back into the double wheelbase transit van. The driver started the engine, revved it several times and then screeched away.

"That could have been nasty," Brian said.

"I told you, didn't I?" Al said.

The brothers waited several minutes before leaving the house, crossing the road and entering house number 52. Inside everything had been turned over and battered. The kitchen units were in pieces on the floor and the door hung on just one hinge. The wall above the fireplace was covered in pellets from the shotgun.

"Probably best we don't mention this to Sandy," Al said as he pulled the front door to a closed position.

Brian shrugged his shoulders.

"Sandy can take care of herself just fine," Brian said as they crossed the road back to the new squat.

Once inside, Al grabbed his coat and wrote 'The Bell Kings Cross' on the back of an envelope and put it through the outside door knocker.

"I think we need a drink," Al said.

Brian beamed.

"You ain't wrong brother," Brian said as they walked down Gloucester Drive.

Once inside the pub, Al went up to the bar and ordered a couple of pints of lager. It was early afternoon and already the pub was packed.

As Al put the lagers on the table, he turned to his right and spotted Tony Mays. He was a huge man that worked out daily to build muscle upon his muscle. When he wasn't training, he would work freelance door security for clubs and music events.

"Give me a minute Brian," Al said before walking across the bar to Tony.

"Hello Tony, how are you mate?" Al said.

Tony smiled.

"So you're back then Al," Tony said.

Al nodded.

"Here to stay," Al said. "I've got a cushy little number if you're interested."

"Is it heavy?" Tony said.

Al shook his head and chuckled.

"There's a brothel in Gloucester Drive run by a Madam called Madge. She's a friend of mine and she's looking for someone to diffuse any aggravation quickly and effectively. I immediately thought of you," Al said.

"I can't imagine there's too much grief in a brothel. It's just geezers looking to get their rocks off," said Tony.

"Precisely, but she wants insurance and she's prepared to pay the right guy three hundred pounds a week," Al said with a wry grin.

"Three hundred quid you say?" Tony said.

Al nodded.

"Plus, there will be other... benefits," Al said.

A smile quickly spread across Tony's face.

"Are you interested?" Al asked.

"Yeah, sure. Why not?" Tony said as he shrugged his shoulders.

"So it wasn't the in-house benefits that swayed you then," Al said with a chuckle.

"Maybe just a little," Tony said.

Al gave Tony the address and asked him to meet with Madge.

"I appreciate this," Tony said. "Can I get you a drink?"

"No, I'm alright thanks," Al said as he stepped away. "I'm with my brother."

As Al walked back to the table, an image of his brother, Wullie torturing Glen the dog suddenly came to mind.

"By rights I should beat the living shit out of you for what you did to my dog," Al thought. *"But I gave my word, and I don't break my word... ever."*

The first pint didn't touch sides and Brian strode over to the bar to order a second with a couple of whiskey chasers.

The pub door opened and in stepped Mae West.

Chapter 15

"**M**ae!" Al called as he jumped to his feet.

"Al McIntosh... It's bloody good to see you!" Mae said as he threw his arms around Al.

Mae joined them at the table.

"It's good to see you too Brian," Mae said.

"Good to see you too," Brian said before taking a large gulp of his lager.

Al reached into his pocket and handed Brian a ten-pound note.

"Do me a favour, would you?" Al said. "Can you get a round of drinks in?"

"Yeah sure," Brian said. "What are you having, Mae?"

"Gin and tonic for me darling," Mae said.

"Make it a double," Al said as he turned to face his friend.

"I wasn't sure that you'd come back to London but then I thought, it's in his blood now," Mae said. "London can do that to a person."

"Glasgow has nothing for me now," Al said.

"Do you have anything on the go?" Mae said softly. "Are you alright for money?"

"I have enough to get me by. Why, do have you something?" Al said.

Mae looked from left to right and then leaned across the table.

"I've got something that's right up your street," Mae whispered.

Al revealed a huge grin.

"Tell me more."

"I got the message."

Al looked up to see Sandy standing there in her heavily studded leather jacket carrying her crash helmet.

"Hi Sandy, this is a really good friend mine, Mae West," Al said.

"Aren't you just divine," Mae said as she shook Sandy's hand.

Brian returned to the table carrying a tray of drinks.

"You found us alright then," Brian said as he put the tray on the table.

"Well I'm here," Sandy said.

"What would you like to drink?" Brian said before taking a quick sip of his lager.

"I don't," Sandy said.

"What, you don't want a drink?"

Sandy shook her head and smiled.

"What do you want then?" Brian asked.

Mae nudged Al's arm and quietly giggled.

"I was looking forward to... fish and chips... or something," Sandy said.

"Oh... okay," Brian said. "You don't want just a quick drink then?"

Sandy slowly shook her head from side to side.

"Right then," Brian said as he put his pint of lager on the table. "I'll probably see you a little bit later."

"Alright Brian," Al said with a sly wink. "Enjoy your... fish and chips or something."

Brian smiled and mouthed 'fuck off' as he followed Sandy out of the pub.

"It must be love," Mae said.

"She is a very smart young lady," Al said as he handed Mae his gin and tonic. "I think Brian has done alright for himself."

Mae took a sip of her drink.

"I spoke to Joe, your boyfriend," Al said. "He seems like a nice fella."

Mae put his drink on the table and then brushed his long blonde wig back off his face.

"He is very special to me," Mae said.

"I'm pleased for you Mae," Al said.

"Do you want to hear about this bit of business?" Mae asked.

"Absolutely," Al said.

"Do you remember Rock Hudson?" Mae asked.

Al nodded.

Rock Hudson was another of the male prostitutes that frequented Soho along with Mae West, Jean Harlow and Harry the Poof.

"Well Rock has this punter with special needs," Mae said before taking a sip of his drink. "He has this jeweller from Hatton Garden. They meet up dressed as cowboys, take poppers and watch blue movies and then have sex."

Al understood Poppers to be the slang term for a chemical drug that is inhaled. They are popular with homosexuals as they cause blood vessel dilation, muscle relaxation and sexual enhancement.

"Okay," Al muttered.

"This jeweller has sixty thousand pounds in his safe," Mae said.

"Sixty thousand pounds!" Al said.

Mae nodded.

"There are sixty bundles and each one has one thousand pounds in it and Rock counted them all. There's sixty thousand pounds in cash just sitting there," Mae said.

"How does Rock know this for sure?" whispered Al.

"The jeweller pays Rock five hundred pounds for the day's sex, and get this," Mae whispered. "The jeweller has given Rock the combination so he could go to the safe and take out the five hundred pounds himself."

Al shook head and exhaled.

Mae took a long swig of her gin and tonic and then reached over for the whiskeys Brian had brought to the table.

"Don't mind if I...?" Mae said.

"No, no," Al said. "Help yourself."

"It's not a complete walk in the park," Mae said.

"Okay. I'm listening," Al said.

"The jeweller has this minder, a monster of a man. He's got to be six foot six inches tall and about the same in width, and has a face like a constipated boxer dog," Mae said.

"No problem, "Al said as he leaned further forward. "I'll take care of that."

Mae swallowed her whiskey and began to laugh.

"That's what I always liked about you, Al, no matter how big a fella is, you just take care of it," Mae said.

"I'm interested," Al said.

Al watched as a tall, medium built man dressed in a handmade suit entered the pub. Immediately three lads got up from a table at the far end of the bar as he approached them.

"Who's that?" Al asked.

Mae glanced over.

"That's Dougie 'The Man' McKinnon," Mae said. "He's the top dog - number one around here."

"He looks like he's just walked straight out of a sixties movie," Al said.

"He does model himself on the old school gangsters," Mae whispered. "I think he sees himself as a Ronnie Kray or Eddy Richardson."

Dougie 'The Man' sat down and was promptly joined by a guy in blue jeans and a white T-shirt. He had short blonde curly hair with a matching moustache and reflective chrome sunglasses.

"Who is the side kick?" Al said.

"That's 'Heart Attack'. Mae said, still speaking softly. "He was a blagger – an armed robber, back in the late sixties until he got weighed off."

"So why do they call him Heart Attack?" Al said as he reached for his drink.

"He's had five heart attacks and survived them all," Mae said. "He can be a nasty piece of work. There are some that call him 'Plant Pot' because he nearly beat some poor fella called Jimmy Wilson to death. It was a down and out liberty. Sadly, Jimmy was dying from tuberculosis and all he did was stick up for himself when Heart Attack started giving him grief."

"Interesting," Al muttered.

"Do you mind if we join you?"

Al looked up to see two smiling young girls. Al caught the eye of the girl that spoke with a soft Irish accent. She had wavy, solferino red hair that tumbled over her shoulders. Her eyes were an intense jade green, and her puffy lips were kiss-inspiring and satin soft.

"By all means, please do," Al said as he motioned for the girls to sit down.

Mae looked at his watch.

"Al, I have an appointment in half an hour, so I need to get myself ready," Mae said as he rose from the table.

"Oh, please don't leave because of us," the second girl said.

Al smiled when he heard the second soft Irish accent. The girl was pretty with lavish star flame-gold hair and intense bliss-blue eyes. He couldn't help but notice her bewitching white teeth when she smiled.

"Two very pretty girls," Al thought.

"Don't mind me sweetheart," Mae said as he patted Al on the shoulder. "I have places to go and people to see. Al, I'll keep you posted about that bit of business."

"Yeah, please do that."

The two girls sat down.

"I'm Al. Can I get you a drink?"

"Hello Al, I'm Cassidy and this is my friend Bridget," Cassidy said as she put her handbag on the table.

"So what's it to be?" Al said as he stood up and rubbed his hands.

"Can I have a vodka and tonic?" Cassidy said with a broad smile.

"Of course you can," Al said.

"I'll have the same, please," Bridget said.

"I won't be a minute," Al said before he side-stepped the adjoining table and went to the bar.

Al ordered two double vodka and tonics, a lager and a whiskey chaser.

"Nice pair of sorts you have there."

Al turned to see Sid.

Sid was a petty thief. He had a history of shoplifting, bag snatching and stealing milk off people's doorsteps.

"You alright Sid," Al said. "Do you want a drink?"

"Yeah go on then, I'll have a lager with you," Sid said.

"Here mate," Al called to the barman. "Stick another pint on there, cheers."

"Do you mind if I...?" Sid said as he nodded towards the two Irish girls.

"No, fine," Al said.

Al carried the tray of drinks back to the table and introduced Sid. The conversation flowed easily, and Al found he was becoming increasingly attracted to Cassidy. She would look over, smile and then quickly avert her gaze.

"I think I could be on here," Al thought as the four of them chinked glasses.

Al thought he felt something touch his foot. He shrugged it off until it happened again. Al looked over at Sid who was tilting his head back and forth towards Bridget.

"I think he wants to know if it's alright to try it on with Bridget," Al thought as he nodded the go ahead.

Al drank the last of his pint in two large gulps and then stood up.

"I need to…" Al said as he nodded towards the men's toilets.

Cassidy giggled and then took a small sip of her drink.

Al stood over the urinal and pointed his manhood towards the porcelain.

"Why is it after you've had that first pee, you know you'll be in again and again?" Al thought.

After shaking himself he washed his hands and returned to the bar. The two girls at the table looked flustered, troubled and concerned.

"Are you girls alright?" Al said as he approached the table.

"No," Cassidy said. "Your friend, Sid, has stolen Bridget's handbag."

"Oh, you're fucking kidding me," Al thought as he sat down.

"Are you sure?" Al said.

"I had it right here," Bridget said. "I have less than five pounds in my purse."

"It's not the money," Cassidy said. "We don't care about the money. Bridget has a photograph of her dead daughter in that bag and it's the only picture she has."

Al could see that Bridget was getting upset.

"Sid, you no good slag!" Al thought. *"You must have thought that I said it was alright to nick Bridget's handbag, not try it on."*

"How long has he been gone?" Al said as he shot up from the table.

"He left shortly after you went to the toilet."

"Come on let's go and find him," Al said as he led the two girls out of the pub.

They trio walked down the road towards a second pub when Al spotted a woman he knew as Nancy 'Fancy Pants' walking towards them with two men. Nancy had been given the name because she always wore the same style of hippie bell bottom trousers.

"Nancy," Al called.

Nancy acknowledged Al by raising her head slightly.

"Have you seen Sid?" Al asked.

"Why, who wants to know?" Nancy Fancy Pants answered cockily.

"We do," Cassidy said as she stepped forward. "He stole my friend's handbag!"

"Who the fuck do you think you are, calling my brother a thief?" Nancy Fancy Pants yelled as she took two steps closer to Bridget.

"You're not Sid's sister," Al thought.

SMACK!

Nancy Fancy Pants surged forward and head-butted Bridget on the nose. She immediately cupped her face and fell onto one knee.

"What the...?" Al thought as he instinctively bent down to help her up.

CRACK!

One of the men with Nancy Fancy Pants kicked Al right in the side of the face. Al immediately got back onto his feet before his attacker could get another kick in. With gritted teeth Al threw a powerful right cross that stunned his opponent and left him open. Al kicked the man three times between the legs before launching a series of vicious left and right jabs. The attacker fell to his knees; his face was bloody, and his hands cupped his genitalia. Al ran forward and kicked him straight in the face.

"You bastard!"

Al turned quickly to see the other man pounding towards him with a metal rod. He lunged with the weapon and Al responded by moving his head and upper body. The metal rod missed his face by millimetres. Al stepped back with both fists clenched when the man screamed and lunged forward again. The metal rod slid along the side of Al's stomach before sinking into the brick wall behind him. Al raised his fists and sent a nasty right hander that cracked the opponent's nose. The man screamed and tugged again on the metal rod. He was wide open for Al to release a combination of left and right jabs to his face and a left hook that threw his chin up in the air. Al lined his victim up for the kill and then threw several heavy head shots and a right hook to the temple. Al stepped back as the man fell to one knee and looked up at the sky with blood pouring from his nose and mouth. With the adrenaline and hate racing through his body Al looked down like a savage tiger on its prey. Al could smell the blood and it was time to finish these two. With his fists tightly clenched, Al powered a right hander that felt like it had rattled his prey's brain. As the man rolled onto the pavement Al fired off a series of body kicks that connected with such ferocity that the limp body raised by several millimetres with every pounding of his foot.

"Leave it out mate," the first attacker called as he tried to get back onto his feet.

Al turned on him. He could see the look of utter fear and astonishment in his eyes.

SMACK!

POW!

CRACK!

Al pounded one kick after another as his prey tried desperately to curl his body and protect his head. He walked around the curled body twice before stopping and smashing his right foot down on the man's head.

"Stop, stop!" Nancy Fancy Pants called. "You're killing them!"

Al stopped and fixed his eyes on her.

Nancy Fancy Pants was frozen to the spot.

"When you see... your brother, Sid," Al said as he fixed his glare firmly on her. "Tell him to bring this girl's handbag and all its contents to the Bell or there will be trouble... for the pair of you."

RING! RING! RING!

Al turned to see an ambulance racing up the road with the bells ringing and lights flashing. He stepped out into the road and stood his ground until the ambulance came to a screeching halt. Al walked around the back of the ambulance and wrenched the back doors open. Inside was a paramedic and an injured patient on an intravenous drip. Al grabbed the first of his victims by the scruff of the neck and dragged him to the back of the ambulance.

"Oi, what the hell is going on here!" the ambulance driver yelled.

Al turned to face the driver with hate and imminent violence in his eyes.

The ambulance driver held up both hands and took two steps back.

Al lifted the limp body and bundled him into the back of the ambulance. The paramedic leapt out and helped Al bring his second severely beaten attacker to the ambulance. The door was slammed shut and the ambulance raced off up the street with lights flashing and bells ringing.

Maureen Flanagan model / actress a firm
Favourite with prison inmates.

The Scottish Stores pub in the Caledonian Road

Argyle Square in Kings Cross aka 'Itchy Park'

The Bell Pub in Pentonville Road

Chapter 16

"**H**ere, Al."

Al turned to see Tony Mays step out of Madge's brothel.

"How's it working out for you?" Al said with a grin.

"Sweet, mate. I appreciate the work," Tony said as he took a packet of cigarettes from his pocket and offered one to Al.

"Nah, I'm alright," Al said shaking his head.

"Al, everyone - and I do mean everyone - is talking about you," Tony said as he lit the cigarette. "Out in the pubs, the punters here last night, and the girls."

"Why?" Al said shrugging his shoulders.

"You are one cool fucker," Tony chuckled.

"I'm not with you," Al said.

"Mate, you smashed seven sorts of shit out of two of the hardest fuckers around here, George McCloughan and Jake McCallum," Tony said before drawing hard on his cigarette.

"I didn't know who they were," Al said.

"George McCloughan and Jake McCallum fucking hate Dougie 'The Man' McKinnon, and I mean hate with a passion. They've been fucking with him for months by chipping a bit of his business here and there. Most thought that it'd only be a matter of time before the pair of them muscle in and take it all. Between you and me mate, even I thought that Dougie 'The Man' McKinnon's days were numbered."

"Like I said, Tony, I didn't know who they were," Al said.

Tony inhaled deeply on his cigarette.

"Well everyone knows who the fuck *you* are now," Tony said. "Anyway, I better crack on. You take care, Al."

"Yeah, you too mate," Al said.

"This could get interesting," Al thought as he marched down Gloucester Drive.

Al opened the door to the Bell and immediately saw Mae sitting at a table by the window.

Al waved and motioned 'want a drink' with his right hand.

Mae smiled and nodded.

Al ordered a double round and took the tray over to Mae's table.

"Mr McIntosh," Mae said with a grin. "Did you notice how everyone looked over when you entered?"

Al took a sip of his lager before shaking his head.

"That altercation with George McCloughan and Jake McCallum hasn't gone unnoticed," Mae said as he chinked his gin and tonic glass on Al's pint. "They are seriously dangerous, heavy duty men and you've put them both in hospital."

"They started it," Al said.

"I think everyone knows the story what with Nancy Fancy Pants running around telling everyone who will listen," said Mae.

"What's her story?" Al said before taking a long sip of his drink.

"She's a brass," Mae said. "She's been working the streets for a few years now, but her big thing is latching on to the top men. Anyone with a bit of muscle and reputation and Nancy Fancy Pants is all over them."

161

"Oh, right," Al said.

"She'll probably be in here later trying to get inside your trousers," Mae said with chuckle.

"She can fuck off," Al said firmly. "I've no interest in that."

"With new girls from John O'Groats to Land's End arriving at Euston, Kings Cross and St Pancras every day, why would you?" Mae said as she put her glass down. "Anyway, I've got some bad news."

Al looked up.

"What?"

"The Hatton Garden Jeweller job... It's off," Mae said quietly.

"Fuck, that's sixty thousand quid," Al hissed. "What happened?"

"You probably didn't know this, but Rock Hudson has been having an on and off thing with Jean Harlow for a while. Well Rock has gone and told Jean about the money in the safe and about knowing the combination and he wanted in. So the pair of them have turned up dressed in their cowboy outfits and this jeweller is thinking that he's going to be having some wild threesome thing. I don't think the jeweller even got out of his trousers before Jean has pulled out this wrought iron fire poker and beat the shit out of him. When the minder has heard all the screaming, he's come running in, only to be beaten to a pulp. Jean left them both in a bad way. So, they've opened the safe, grabbed the money and made their escape," Mae said. "The sad thing is they didn't even get a chance to spend any of it!"

"What happened?" Al said.

"They left their fingerprints all over the place. It was only hours before the police kicked the door in and nicked the pair of them red-handed with the money and the weapon. They've been carted off to Pentonville and I heard this morning that there's no bail. They could be looking at eight years."

"At least, I would have thought," Al said before taking a quick glimpse around the bar.

"Gutted," Al said. "I'm gutted for them, and for not getting that nice bit of work."

"There will be others," Mae said.

"There always is," Al said.

YAH! YAH!

"What the...?" Al said as he turned to see an old fella clamber up onto a pub table, thrust his hips and then slowly undo the button and zip of his trousers.

"What's he playing at?" Al said with a chuckle.

Mae laughed out loud.

"That's Old Dickie Boyd," Mae said.

Old Dickie pulled down his trousers, thrust his hips again while yelling 'Yah, Yah' and then slowly pulled down his off-white underwear. Old Dickie grabbed his manhood and began waving it about.

"That's his party trick," Mae said as he nodded towards Dickie and a scruffy looking fella sitting at the table Dickie was standing on. "Old Dickie and Rab are war veterans. They both served overseas in the Second World War. They came home and started breaking into safes until it came on top and they were shipped off at Her Majesty's pleasure. These days they both beg for change down at Kings Cross and then spend what they get in here, getting pissed up. Old Dickie with his cock hanging out means that he's had a good day."

163

Al watched as the old fella pulled up his trousers while a few of the regulars happily cheered.

"He has this one story that he just loves to tell over and over," Mae said.

"Go on," Al said, urging him to tell the story.

"Well, it normally starts with Old Dickie saying how he would shag the convicts he was banged up with before leading on to his claim to fame," Mae said before taking a quick sip of his drink. "So, Dickie is begging outside Kings Cross Station and low and behold, Richard Burton passes through the station."

"Richard Burton as in Richard Burton and Elizabeth Taylor?" Al said.

"You got it," Mae said as he glanced over at Old Dickie being helped off the table. "Dickie has spotted him and asked for some change. Well, according to Dickie, Richard has stopped and engaged him in a conversation before inviting him back for a couple of vodkas at an apartment."

"Nah," Al said in disbelief.

"That's not all," Mae said.

"Well go on," Al said.

"After Dickie has finished his second vodka, Richard pulls fifty quid out of his wallet and hands it over and tells him to fuck off and never try to beg from him again."

"Do you believe it?" Al said with a snigger.

"It's possible," Mae said. "He certainly enjoys telling the story."

"Then that's all that matters then," Al said.

"Oh, by the way, I saw Harry the Poof last night," Mae said before swallowing the last of his gin and tonic. "He said to send you his best."

Al remembered Harry the Poof from the last time he was in London. He was a male prostitute working Soho. Harry had a vicious temper and specialised in blackmailing his clients.

"Tell him I said hello back."

"Al McIntosh."

Al looked up see a gargantuan figure standing by their table

"Al pushed his chair back and clenched both fists under the table.

"I'm Big Jim Gibson. Can I have a word?"

"Al, I need to be off," Mae said.

"I'll catch you later," Al said, motioning Big Jim Gibson to sit down.

Big Jim Gibson held his hand out across the table. Al hesitated for a moment and then shook it.

"You've impressed a number of people with how you dealt with George McCloughan and Jake McCallum," Big Jim Gibson said as he leaned back in the chair.

"So say what you've got to say and then fuck off," Al thought as he listened. *"I don't like or trust you matey."*

"You've come to the attention of Dougie 'The Man' McKinnon and he'd like to meet you," Big Jim Gibson said.

"Okay," Al said.

"You're invited to his table," Big Jim Gibson said as he turned and nodded towards a table at the far end of the bar. "Only a somebody gets invited to sit with 'The Man'."

Al rose to his feet.

"Come on then," Al said as he pushed the chair back under the table.

Big Jim Gibson led him through the pub to the table where Dougie 'The Man' McKinnon was sitting alone with a large glass tumbler.

"Al, it's a pleasure to meet you," Dougie said, holding out his hand.

"You too," Al said, admiring his smart tailor-made suit.

"Please, join me."

Al smiled and sat in the chair opposite him

"Jim, go and get us a bottle of whiskey," Dougie 'The Man' McKinnon said without looking up.

"Sure thing, boss," Big Jim said as he scampered off to the bar.

"I was impressed with how you took care of George McCloughan and Jake McCallum," Dougie said matter of factly.

"I probably saved you from a good kicking, you mean," Al thought.

"Pair of chancers," Dougie said as he slid a glass tumbler towards Al. "Always pushing their luck."

"A bit more than that from what I've been hearing," Al thought.

"There you go," Big Jim said as he put the open bottle of Johnny Walker on the table.

Dougie 'The Man' raised the bottle and poured out three drinks.

"It was only a matter of time before someone gave them a good hiding," Dougie 'The Man' said as he raised his glass. "Cheers."

"Cheers," Al said before taking a sip from his glass.

"Yeah, cheers," Big Jim said.

"They were both on my radar," Dougie 'The Man' said.

"Well you should have taken care of them then," Al thought.

"Tell me, Al," Dougie 'The Man' said as he turned to face Al. "What do you know about me?"

"I'm told you're the top man," Al said calmly.

"That would be right," Dougie 'The Man' said firmly. "I am the fucking man and there's trouble, a whole truck load of trouble, for anyone who fucks with what is mine."

Al took another sip of his whiskey.

"In addition to the Bell I also run The Earl of Russell, Scottish Doors, Prince Albert, Queens Head, The Albion, The Dolphin, The Rising Sun on Euston Road and The Hole in the Wall," Dougie 'The Man' said as he reached into his pocket and produced a small bag of white powder.

"So you run all the pubs within a mile of here," Al thought. *"Is that cocaine?"*

Dougie 'The Man' placed a little of the powder between his clasped finger and thumb and then sniffed deeply.

"Do you like a bit of Charlie?" Dougie said.

"I'm alright with my drink thanks," Al replied.

"I think a man like you could do well working with us," said Dougie 'The Man' before taking a second snort of the white powder.

"I'll have a good look at how your operation works," Al thought as he smiled attentively at Dougie 'The Man'. *"There is no way I'm going to work for you and Big Jim Gibson... I don't fucking like you much either."*

"Hello boys."

Al looked up to see a large flamboyant looking guy wearing a smart blue suit with a red Welsh dragon embroidered on his top pocket.

"Leaky, take a seat," Dougie 'The Man' said as he slid the bottle of whiskey towards him. "This is another one of my gang."

Al couldn't help but notice the sudden look of shock on Leaky's face.

"You would never believe that our Welsh friend here is a rich man in his own right," Dougie 'The Man' said. "His father died and left him over a hundred grand in cash and a house worth about the same but Leaky here sold it and turned his back on the family business to become... a villain."

"What can I say," Leaky said with a chuckle. "Some men aspire to be captains of industry while others, like me, want nothing more than to be a thief and live the life that comes with it."

"Good to meet you Leaky," Al said as he reached across the table and shook his hand. "I'm Al McIntosh."

"I know who you are Al... everyone knows who you are." Leaky said. "I print money, well fivers, and if I do say so myself... my work is good."

"That's good to know," Al said.

"Leaky is a dab hand with a blade too," Big Jim Gibson said.

Laky frowned a little before smiling.

"Not just any blade," Leaky said as he opened his jacket, revealing a leather holster. "I like Bowie Knives."

A Bowie knife is a five-to-twelve-inch fixed blade fighting knife created by Rezin Bowie in the early 19th century for his brother, Jim Bowie, who had become famous for his duel known as the Sandbar Fight.

"I've got quite a collection," Leaky said.

"Go on show him," Big Jim said. "Show Al what you can do."

"Really," Leaky said, shrugging his shoulders.

"Go on, show Al," Dougie 'The Man' said bluntly.

Leaky pushed his chair back and stood up. He reached into his jacket and produced a huge Bowie Knife.

"Al," Leaky said as he pointed the knife at the dart board. "Pick a number."

Al turned to the old pub dart board which was a good twelve feet away.

"Twenty," Al said.

"Double or Triple," Leaky asked as he swiftly moved his hand down onto the blade.

"Triple," Al said.

Leaky threw the knife instantly and it plunged deep into the dart board's triple twenty, breaking the slim steel wire.

"Impressive," Al said.

"I've been practising my knife throwing skills for hours every day for years.

I like this Welsh fella," Al thought as he peered down at the dart board.

Leaky reached into his pocket and produced a couple of pills that Al instantly recognised as Black Bombers. Leaky winked as he put both the tablets in his mouth.

Leaky returned to the gathering, placed his knife back inside the holster, sat down and then put a white plastic carrier bag on the table.

Dougie suddenly shot up and looked down at his gold Rolex watch.

"Jim, we have to do the rounds," Dougie 'the Man' said before taking a final snort of cocaine. "You're welcome to my table any time, Al."

"Cheers," Al said as he watched Dougie 'The Man' McKinnon and Big Jim Gibson strut across the pub like Gangsters from a James Cagney movie.

"You two are a pair of self-absorbed mugs," Al thought.

Chapter 17

Al and Leaky had got on extremely well the day before and agreed to meet up for a drink at The Bell the following day.

"How do you get on with Dougie?" Al said with an air of caution in his tone.

"He's alright," Leaky said, then lowered his voice. "I am not in his gang and do not work for him. I do my own thing and every so often we do a bit of business."

"I'm looking around this pub and thinking there's a fortune being made," Al said.

"Dougie doesn't tax anyone in the Bell," Leaky said. "He may take a slice of the action in his other pubs but nothing in here."

"The bloke's a bigger mug than I first thought," Al thought. *"What you have, 'Dougie the fucking man McKinnon', is a Mickey Mouse operation. There must be thousands to be had out of here week in week out."*

"Well I never," Leaky said. "Take a look at him."

Al looked up to see an older guy in his seventies wearing a brown suit with a large-collared shirt open to the waist revealing a gold medallion on a chain. There were three girls in short summer dresses and heels with him.

"Who is that?" Al said with a giggle.

"You have to love old Charlie," Leaky said. "He has a heart of gold. His missus passed away about a year, maybe eighteen months ago, and Charlie befriended some of the girls working the streets. After hearing about one of the girls getting beaten up by some punter, old Charlie has invited four of his favourite girls to move in with him. The girls have their own room and a separate phone so they can still see their regulars. I'm pretty sure they're bunging him a couple of quid because he wasn't looking that dapper the last time I saw him. The girls all call him Charlie's Angels."

"Fair play to him," Al said.

"Charlie, I can only imagine what your wife will be saying to you on the other side when you eventually pop your clogs," Al thought. *"I reckon you'll be in big trouble but... good for you!"*

"You must be Al."

Al turned to his right to see a young lad with a military style haircut, wearing blue jeans and a white t-shirt.

"I am," Al said cautiously. "How can I help you?"

"Everyone calls me SAS," the lad said, as he held out his right arm showing a 'Who Dares Wins' tattoo.

Leaky nudged Al.

"Oh, right," Al said. "So you've had the SAS emblem tattooed on your arm?"

"I have some great memories with the lads," SAS said, puffing out his chest.

Leaky nudged Al again...twice.

"Well, it's good to meet you. SAS you say," Al said with a wry grin.

"That's right, after the Special Air Service," SAS said as he displayed the tattoo on his right arm for the second time.

"Look, SAS, I'm in a bit of a business meeting at the moment, so do you mind?" Al said as he nodded his head to the right.

"Of course, mum's the word," SAS said before strutting off towards the bar.

"What the fuck was that all about?" Al said with a chuckle.

"Al, he's harmless," Leaky said. "He's been coming in here for years telling his stories about being dropped in behind enemy lines and the truth is, the lad has never served a day in the army in his life. But that said, he's harmless and everyone likes him... well, tolerates him."

The pub door opened and several new girls walked in.

"Have you noticed how many new girls there are around the place?" Al said.

Leaky nodded.

"They're arriving from all over the country," Leaky said. "The police and politicians would have you believe that these girls are being forced into the sex trade by vicious nasty pimps, but that simply isn't the truth. I don't know of a single pimp operating anywhere around Kings Cross. These girls have husbands, boyfriends and children at home. They've been driven here by poverty. A girl arrives at Kings Cross, Euston or St Pancras and immediately goes into a local pub and it's not long before she has her first punter. A week later she goes back home with a purse full of cash to put food on the table for her family and pays the bills. The following week she is back again, only this time she's brought down a friend or a sister and so it goes on."

"Leaky, did you hear what happened to Auld Rab Donnelly?"

Leaky turned to a short girl in blonde pig tails and a white short skirt.

"He was in here last night absolutely pissed," Leaky said.

"That's right. He had a blinding day begging by all accounts which was why he was in here pissing it up. Anyway, when he's staggered home he's opened the door to the squat he was staying at, and he's gone straight through where the floor should have been. The poor sod has smashed up both his legs. He's in a right state."

"What do you mean the floor that should have been there?" Al said.

"The council came around during the day and took out all the floorboards so when he's gone home in the dark he's just fallen straight down into the cellar."

"That's fucking out of order," Al said.

"I'll pop by the hospital," Leaky said. "Thanks for letting me know."

"Here, get yourself a drink," Leaky said as he slid several five-pound notes towards her.

"Thanks, Leaky."

After the girl left the table, Al turned to Leaky and whispered.

"You're not passing forged fivers in here, are you?"

Leaky shook his head emphatically.

"Not in a million years," Leaky said. "Lucy is a working girl. Later tonight she might charge some punter say, fifteen quid for a blow job in his motor. Once the deed is done, he'll give her a twenty-pound note, and she'll hand him back that fiver as change."

Al's attention was drawn to a loud, raucous laugh at the bar.

"I know that laugh," Al thought. *"That's Large William. I met him in Pentonville."*

"Can you give me a minute, Leaky, I've just seen an old mate," Al said as he rose from the table.

"Yeah, no problem I've got some printing to do anyway," Leaky said with a wink.

Al walked across the pub quietly and stopped directly behind his friend.

"Name and number to the Guvnor!" Al yelled.

174

Large William swivelled around. His face lit up when he saw Al.

"Fuck me it's you, Al!" Large William said as he threw his arm around his friend.

"Hello mate, how are you?"

"All the better for seeing you, Al!" Large William said. "Let's grab a table."

As Al walked back to his table he glanced over to where Big Jim Gibson was sitting with his girlfriend. Big Jim was busy relaying a story, but his girlfriend's gaze homed in on Al. She slowly parted her legs, revealing a white triangle.

"What the fuck?" Al thought as he quickly averted his gaze

"It's good to see you on the outside," Al said.

"Eight years is a long time to be banged up," Large William said.

"Are you alright for money?" Al said as he reached into his trouser pocket.

Large William raised his huge hand.

"I'm alright, but I do appreciate the sentiment mate."

Large William looked around him and then leaned forward over the table.

"I've gone straight back to work with the same firm," Large William said. "We've been mates since school, and I trust them."

"What, you're hi-jacking trucks?" Al whispered.

"Fags, booze, electrical gear, you name it, and we nick it by the truck load," Large William said as he sat back in the chair and expanded his chest.

"Do you take orders?"

"Sure, a waiting customer is the best kind of business. What do you want?" Large William said.

"I'm alright for now," Al said. "Do you have a telephone number where I can contact you?"

Chapter 18

Al was just one of scores of the Bell's customers reading their Sunday newspapers while sipping on their pints.

"Have you been reading this?" Leaky said as he put his newspaper on the table.

"It's telling us what we already know," Al said as he folded his newspaper. "Girls from all over the country are travelling down to the capital to sell sex."

"I've seen it grow tenfold in the last few months, but now, after making this national reading in a Sunday scandal rag, this place will be ram packed with punters looking for girls and girls looking for money," Leaky said.

"There's got to be some money in this somewhere," Al thought as he looked around the pub at the new faces.

"Leaky do you mind if I ask you something?" Al said.

"Sure, go ahead." Leaky replied as he pulled out a chair and sat down.

"From what Dougie 'The Man' McKinnon was saying, this isn't a life that you had to have what with your Da leaving you money and property," Al said.

"True," Leaky said.

"Then why would you choose to be a flamboyant villain?"

"I've learnt that people want two things in life," Leaky said as he sat back in his chair. "The first is love. Now, not all of us will have the whole falling in love thing, so we settle for a connection. For me that would be working girls. I like to have fun followed by adventurous sex. At the end I pay for the service. My connection is customer and supplier. We both get exactly what we want, we're both happy, and on that basis we do it again and again."

Al nodded and unfolded his arms.

"Don't get me wrong, some people out there are just mean arseholes. They go out of their way to pull someone in to like them, maybe even fall in love, and then hurt them in the worst possible way and move on. Probably like you Al, we've both seen and know people that are like that. I believe that those abusers end up getting hurt themselves in later life."

"I've certainly come across a few like that," Al said as he stroked his chin.

"The second thing we are all looking for is self-actualisation. I looked at my father and his friends, and their life looked dull, tedious and something that was never going to be for me. When I think of the villainous lifestyle it's romanticised because those in the game look like they're in control and can influence the outcome of any situation. Villains, real hard-core villains, use weapons and can have a fight, or at the very least look like they can. If you look around a room full of villains, you can see by their actions that they have access to lots of money because they're willing to balance risk and reward and take what they want. People like us live by our own set of rules and will draw first blood should someone break our moral code. We understand that the politicians, police and the entire system is managed to keep the masses under control. I didn't want to work a forty-hour week, pay my taxes, get married and have children then wait for retirement. I want to feel excitement from the moment I open my eyes in the morning until I close them at night. My choice is to live on the edge with the adrenaline racing through my veins and risk imprisonment, if necessary, to feel fully alive. For me, Al, that is self-actualisation and I get to enjoy it every day."

"That was deep," Al said raising his eyebrows.

"What about you Al?"

"My life of crime started with a box of Mars Bars... It's a long story," Al said.

Al's attention was drawn to the bar where he spotted Big Jim Gibson's girlfriend. She turned, smiled and held his gaze for a few moments.

"Leaky, what's the score with Big Jim Gibson's girlfriend?" Al whispered.

"Trouble Al, that girl is a full on flirt," Leaky said. "Jim loves Carol but all she loves is this whole lifestyle we've just been talking about. You're the new major face on the manor and I suspect Carol wants some of you."

Al couldn't help but turn back to Carol at the bar. She was talking enthusiastically with three girls, turned and flicked her hair, smiled and turned back to her friends.

"Well, that was about as blatant as it gets," Leaky said with a sigh. "She'll be over here in a minute. You mark my words."

"I hope not," said Al. "There is no shortage of women available in here without any of the drama."

"Girls like Carol love a bit of drama," Leaky said as he turned to face her. "She's dangerous."

"I'll go and get some drinks in," Al said as he rose from the table.

Al purposely walked over to the opposite end of the bar to Carol. He placed his order and turned to see a working girl he recognised behind him.

"Alright," Al said

"Yeah, you?" the girl said.

Al nodded.

"It's Al, isn't it?"

Al nodded again.

"I'm Trudy, do you want to buy a Rolex watch?" Trudy said as she pulled out a men's stainless-steel Daytona from her handbag.

Al glanced down at the watch.

"Yours for five hundred quid," Trudy said firmly.

Al shook his head and chuckled.

"I'm not looking for a watch, and five hundred pounds, Trudy, is a tourist price."

"Excuse me."

Al turned to see a young guy in a red polo shirt and jeans.

"Yes mate?" Al said.

"I'm interested in the watch if you're not."

"Go for it," Al said as he stepped back so that Trudy faced her potential customer.

"Your friend is right about the price you want, but I'm happy to give you a hundred pounds, in cash, right now."

"Done," Trudy said.

Al watched as the young lad peeled off a hundred pounds and took possession of the watch.

"I'm Mikey Benson and I'm always in the market for prestigious timepieces. That can be Rolex, Cartier, Breitling, I'm sure you know the kind of thing I mean. If it's branded and the price is right, I'll always have them."

Trudy looked him up and down, smiled and left the bar.

"Some of these girls must be robbing their punters," Al thought.

As Al reached for the tray of drinks, he felt someone touch his arm

"Are you going to buy me a drink then Al?"

It was Carol. She reached up and straightened his shirt collar.

"Is Big Jim not here then?" Al said.

"He doesn't have a leash on me," Carol said with a suggestive smile. "I do like to go out and play on my own sometimes."

"I'm sure Big Jim doesn't see it quite like that," Al said as he took a single step away.

"I would have thought a big bad boy like you wouldn't worry about Big Jim or anyone else," Carol said, fixing her gaze on him and taking a step closer.

"I'm in a meeting," Al said as he turned to face Leaky. "Enjoy the rest of your day Carol."

"I will be seeing you again," Carol purred before returning to her friends.

"Leaky, she made it quite clear that's she's game," Al said.

"Like I said, dangerous," Leaky said.

"I'm not interested," Al said. "That's not because I'm concerned about Big Jim Gibson. He doesn't bother me at all."

"You're sussing things out... aren't you?" Leaky said with a broad grin.

Al looked Leaky straight in the eyes.

"There is big money to be made around here and the clock is ticking," Al said.

"Well if I can help in anyway," Leaky said. "Just let me know."

"Leaky, I've got some bad news."

It was Lucy.

"I stopped off at the hospital this morning and Auld Rab Donnelly is dead," Lucy said, lowering her head.

"You're joking," Leaky said. "I was only with him yesterday."

"The doctor told me that gangrene had set in," Lucy said.

"This will hit old Dickie Boyd hard. They served in the war together, blew safes and did time at the same nick," Leaky muttered. "What a shitty way to go."

"This is all because the council took up the floorboards. Those bastards knew what they were doing!" Al said as he thumped the table.

"Bastards," Lucy said.

"Yeah, fucking bastards," Leaky said as he punched his fist into his open hand.

"Aren't their offices out on the Essex Road?" Al said as he shot up from the table.

"Yeah," Leaky said.

"Well let's go and make them pay," Al said calmly.

"Alright," Leaky said, nodding.

"Yeah," Lucy said.

"Oi, SAS," Al called out across the bar.

"We've got a mission and you're with me," Al said.

SAS's face lit up. He put his drink on the bar and bounded over to join Al, Leaky and Lucy.

Al led them out of the bar and out onto the street where they marched up to the Essex Road. Several of the regulars joined them as word quickly spread of Auld Rab Donnelly's passing. Al led the crew across the road to the council offices. A taxi driver hooted at having to stop. Leaky turned back and brought his clenched fist down hard on the taxi driver's roof. Al reached down and picked up a large stone, took aim and threw it straight at the office block window. It shattered. Suddenly, stones, bricks and a broken street bin were all being thrown through the windows, shattering glass into the offices and down on the pavement.

Al stood back and looked at the carnage.

"Do you think that Auld Rab Donnelly would appreciate that?" Al said as he turned to Leaky.

"He would, Al," Leaky replied. "He certainly would."

"We need to make a move before it's on us," Al said as he began to jog away down the street with twelve of his co-conspirators behind him.

They crossed the street as one mob and pounded the pavement back to Caledonian Road where they crashed through the Bell's door.

"Get all this lot a drink," Al said to the barman.

He turned to Lucy. "As for you... good job... bloody good job."

Al turned back to the barman and handed him a bundle of notes.

"That was fucking great!" SAS said as he reached for his pint.

"There you go," Al thought. *"Now you have a real story to embellish."*

"Make sure that Lucy doesn't pay for another drink for the rest of the day

---

Al had asked Mae West, Harry the Poof, Brian and Sandy to meet him at an empty house in Finsbury.

"So, what's going on?" Mae said as he looked around the room. "Why are we here?"

Al smiled.

"Do you know what a Shebeen is?" Al asked.

"I do," Brian said.

Mae and Harry the Poof both shrugged their shoulders.

"In Scotland we would call an illegal drinking den a Shebeen," Al said as he looked around the room.

"We call them Speelers down south," Harry the Poof said. "Where is this going?"

"I'm going to open a Shebeen, or as you call it a Speeler, right here, and it's going to be called 'The American Bar'."

"Yeah," Brian said as his face lit up.

"I've got it all worked out," said Al.

"I bet you have," Mae said with a broad grin. "Well come on then."

"I know a guy who runs with a team that hi-jacks truck-loads of booze and fags," Al said as he shifted his gaze from one person to another. "We've had a meet up and I'll have all the cheap booze a Speeler could want within a week or so."

"I'm liking this," Brian said.

"In the last few months hundreds if not thousands of girls have arrived at Kings Cross, St Pancras and Euston from all over the country," Al said as he put his hands in his pockets. "The Sunday newspapers are even writing about it. At the same time the place has been crawling with new faces. These are men looking for a good time and the girls are happy to provide it for a price. My plan is to offer free protection to the brothels and encourage the girls to use here as the meeting place. If a pub charges a pound for a whiskey, then I'll be charging a fiver. With that kind of profit the girls will get a cut of every drink their punter buys. Then once a week they'll get a payment. Men like pretty girls. Night clubs exist because the pretty girls bring the men in who in turn spend money. It's the same principle, only everyone makes money or gets what they want.

"I like it," Brian said.

"Sounds good to me," Harry the Poof said before turning to Mae.

"How can we help?" Mae said.

"I need you to get the word out to the girls," Al said, breaking into a broad smile as he lifted a sledgehammer from the floor. "The place will need to be painted and carpeted, curtains put up, and I've put the word out that I want a bar, but for right now that wall needs knocking down to make the room larger."

Al held out the sledgehammer.

Mae took the hammer and turned to the wall. He raised it high above his head, let out a roar, and smashed the hammer deep into the wall."

Al and Brian let out a spontaneous cheer as the first of the bricks fell onto the floor.

"I can help with the painting," Sandy said, raising her hand.

"I can a work a brush if it helps," Harry the Poof said.

"Thanks," Al said as he watched Mae smash clean through the wall with a third mighty strike. "We'll have a big open night, bring everyone in and make it fun!"

"I do love a good party," Mae said as he handed the sledgehammer to Brian. "Go on Brian, show us what you're made of."

Brian rolled up his shirt sleeves and grabbed the hammer firmly with both hands.

THUD! THUD! THUD!

Brian battered the wall with relentless vigour. The bricks and plaster fell to the floor.

***

After a full day working to get the 'American Bar' underway Al, Brian and Sandy went to the Bell to have a drink. Mae had arranged a date night with his boyfriend Joe, and Harry the Poof had a client to meet.

"I think you're on to a winner," Brian said as he reached for his drink.

"Providing I don't get let down with the bar, it'll be open within a week or two," Al said before taking a long sip of his lager. "The booze is in storage and has already been paid for."

"Al."

Al looked up to see Big Jim Gibson.

"What the fuck does he want?" Al thought.

"Jim," Al said.

"Dougie 'The Man' McKinnon wants a word," Big Jim said in an ominous tone.

Al turned and looked down at the bar to Dougie's usual table. He was sat drinking with Heart Attack.

"Who the fuck does he think he is?" Al thought. *"The Krays and the Richardsons all rolled into one?"*

"Alright." Al said as he got up from the table.

Big Jim stepped back anxiously.

"You need to calm down," Al said with a wry grin. "Or they'll be calling you Heart Attack too."

Big Jim smiled awkwardly.

Al followed him through the pub.

"Alright Al," Tony Mays called out.

Al smiled.

"Cheers Al," SAS said, raising his glass.

Seven people had acknowledged Al during his short walk between the tables.

"Big Jim said you wanted a word," Al said calmly.

"Take a seat, Al," Heart Attack said.

Al pulled out a chair and sat down.

"We've been hearing things," Heart Attack said.

"You'll need to be a bit more specific," Al said, fixing his stare on Heart Attack.

"It's good that you're earning," Dougie 'The Man' McKinnon said. "We hear that you've got something big on."

"Big?" Al said as he turned to stare at Dougie.

"Yeah, some kind of enterprise," Dougie said.

"Well you know what this place can be like for rumours," Al said.

"Is there anything that we can help you with?" Dougie said.

"I have a little something," Al said. "It's not big, but it is a little something."

"I suppose big is relative," Dougie said.

"I know where you're going with this," Al thought.

"Don't misunderstand us," Dougie said. "We like to hear that our friends and partners have ventures, no matter how big or small."

"You're trying to cut yourself in," Al thought as he remained stone faced. *"Well, you can fuck off because this will be my thing."*

"I just want to make sure that everyone is happy," Dougie said.

"Like I said, it's just a little something and I have everything under control," Al said firmly. "I appreciate your offer of help, but I don't need it."

Heart Attack shook his head slowly.

"Then we wish you well," Dougie said as he held out his hand for Al to shake. "We just want everybody to be happy."

Chapter 20

"This place is heaving," Brian said as he poured two glasses of whiskey.

It was the opening night for Al's American Bar.

"It's lucky we knocked the wall down into next door's place," Brian said. "There is no way we could have fitted all these people into just the one room.

Al looked around his Speeler. Just as he had seen the vision in his mind, he was now witnessing the reality. There were scores of very attractive young girls in short skirts and heels and wall to wall punters buying drinks left, right, and centre. No one, not a single person, complained about the vastly overpriced drinks. A system had been put in place so that for every drink a girl's punter buys, she would be rewarded at the end of the week with a commission. The girls were happily throwing drinks down their necks along with the punters.

'Do Ya Think I'm Sexy,' by Rod Stewart began to play through the large, stolen, Wharfedale speakers Al had installed in the corner of the bar.

"Turn it up," one girl called.

"Yeah, turn it up," another called.

Suddenly almost everyone in the bar was calling for the volume to be turned up.

Al walked down the bar with a massive grin on his face and turned the volume up. The bar erupted with cheers.

"If you want my body, and you think I'm sexy, come on sugar let me know," several girls huddled together and began to sing the chorus at the top of their voices while others danced around suggestively.

"If you really need me just reach out and touch me, come on honey tell me so, tell me so baby."

"This is fucking brilliant!" Brian shouted before knocking back his whiskey in one.

The record came to an end and the punters flocked to the bar to order more drinks.

'Ring My Bell,' by Anita Ward began to play. Al reached over and it turned it down.

"I have a confession," one guy in his early thirties called out. He was dressed in a blue pin-stripe suit and wore a white shirt with the collar open to his hairy chest.

His friends gathered around him.

"Well come on then Timothy, spill the beans," yelled one of his friends before swallowing his drink and waving Al's barman over to serve him another.

"This is a secret, right, so no one must tell a soul," Timothy said as he drunkenly placed his finger over his nose.

"Yeah, just me and the other hundred or so punters will hear it," Al thought.

"Come on then," another punter called.

"Right," Timothy said, inhaling deeply. "I have been fucking my boss's wife!"

"You're kidding," his friend said with a shocked expression.

"Bollocks have you," another said. "She's well out of your league!"

191

"True," Timothy said, "and there's more."

"What?"

"He watched and got off on it!" Timothy said, as he thrust out his chest out.   .

Al smirked when he saw the shocked expression on Timothy's friend's faces.

"It takes all sorts in the world," Al thought.

"How do you think I got my promotion?" Timothy said before emptying the contents of his glass in one shot.

"I have a confession too," a guy standing close by called.

"What, worse than that?" Timothy's friend cried.

"My wife was having an affair with my best mate and then fucked off with him!"

"Hey mate, I'm sorry to hear that," Timothy said. "Get this man a drink."

"I don't miss the moaning old cow one bit, but I don't half miss my mate!"

All the lads cheered and raised their glasses.

'I Will Survive,' by Gloria Gaynor began to play.

The looks from the girls told Al that he needed to get that volume turned up and to get it up quickly.

Almost all the working girls, Mae West and his friend, Candy Cain, a transvestite, all bunched up together and began yelling out the lyrics at the top of their voices.

'First, I was afraid, I was petrified

Kept thinking I could never live without you by my side

But then I spent so many nights thinking how you did me wrong

And I grew strong

And I learned how to get along'

Every girl in the American Bar sang along until the final verse. They then dispersed and went back to their punters with an empty glass.

"You have nailed this," Mae West said as he wiped the sweat from his brow and rearranged the blonde wig.

"Everyone is getting what they want," Al said. The girls are earning, and the punters are having a night they'll remember."

"I'm thinking about putting a couple of slot machines in," Al said as he pointed over to some space at the far end of the room.

"Sounds good," Mae said as he looked around the Speeler. "I think we were lucky that the house didn't fall in after taking the wall to next door out."

"Nah, it'll be fine," Al said, brushing it off.

Al spotted a stunning black girl standing by the bar just a few feet from him. He couldn't help noticing that she had one green eye and one brown eye. He found himself turning several times to see if she was still there.

"Who is that girl?" Al said to Mae, nodding in her direction.

Mae looked over and smiled when he saw who Al was looking at.

"That's Black Sandra, she's a lovely girl and very smart," Mae said. "She has six girls and they all work private sex shows for a select clientele. You know the kind of thing. A lesbian show and then pull out a couple of excited city gents who haven't had sex since the last roll on and roll off Saturday night special."

Al turned back to see Black Sandra chatting with a blonde girl.

"Black Sandra is bisexual," Mae whispered. "She will only have sex with white men or white girls and that's it."

Al's eyebrows raised instantly.

"A very sad thing happened to her a couple of weeks ago," Mae said.

"What's that?" Al said as he topped up Mae's glass.

"She was raped and got beaten up pretty badly," Mae said. "She may look alright now, but believe me she was in a bad way."

"I just can't get my head around that," Al said. "Why would you want to hurt a girl who has just agreed to have sex with you?"

"Al, it takes all sorts... believe me," Mae said.

"I was just thinking that," Al thought.

"I bet," Timothy called out, "that I could juggle three bottles of beer for one whole minute while sitting on a chair.

"Fiver says you can't," his friend shouted out.

"I'll have a tenner on that," another called out.

"I'll have twenty quid," Mae said as he turned to Candy Caine and winked.

"You're all on," Timothy said as he pulled out a chair and sat down in the middle of the bar.

The crowd grew around him with *'Rivers of Babylon'* by Boney M playing in the background. Brian brought out three bottles of Watneys Light Ale.

"You break them, you buy them," Brian said.

"Done," Timothy said as he turned the bottles around so he could handle their neck shaft.

"Let's count him in," Mae called out.

Timothy straightened his back and took a deep breath.

Five...four...three...two...one...go!

Timothy launched one bottle into the air with his right hand and caught it with his left. Then as the bottle reached the top of its arc, he introduced a second bottle.

The drunken crowd cheered him on.

Candy Caine had manoeuvred himself around the bar so that he was now directly behind Timothy as he sat on the chair juggling.

Timothy introduced the third bottle and called out for his friend to start the stopwatch. Meanwhile Candy Caine was hitching his dress up. The crowd could see what was happening and began to applaud and whistle with excitement. Candy Caine now had his dress pulled up around his waist exposing black stockings, suspenders and bright red panties. Timothy beamed as he expertly juggled the bottles. Candy pulled his red panties to one side. His huge eight-inch limp cock fell out. The punters and the girls became increasingly animated as Candy stroked it back and forth until it was erect. Timothy juggled, completely unaware of what was happening behind him. Candy, with his throbbing, erect, manhood, took a small step forward and placed it firmly on Timothy's shoulder. The crowd erupted with gasps, cheering and tears of laughter. Timothy glanced to his left only to discover a huge pulsating cock just inches from his face. He lost his balance and the bottles dropped to the floor as he hurled himself to the right.

Candy Caine took a bow as the punters and the girls all clapped wildly.

"Now that is my kind of girl," an elderly city gent cried out before downing his whiskey.

"So buy her a drink," Mae said as she motioned Candy to join them.

"I think I will."

With *'When You're in Love with a Beautiful Woman'* by Dr Hook playing in the background, Black Sandra approached Al.

"This is a great Speeler you have here," Black Sandra said in a broad cockney accent. "You'll do well darling."

"Cheers," Al said. "Drink?"

"Go on then," Black Sandra said as she held out her empty glass tumbler. "I've seen you down at the Bell."

"I enjoy a drink in a few pubs, but the Bell would be my regular," Al said.

"You're a cracking looking girl," Al thought as he inhaled her perfume.

"People are saying that you are the go-to man," Black Sandra said as her eyes met Al's.

"I wouldn't know anything about that," Al said, smiling.

"Could you get me something?" Black Sandra said.

"That would depend."

Black Sandra took a step closer to Al and lowered her voice.

"I need a shooter and bullets."

Al was a little taken back.

"You want a gun?"

"Some dirty bastard raped me a few weeks back and he needs to pay," Black Sandra hissed through gritted teeth.

"Fuck this for a game of soldiers," Al thought. *"Shooters and vendettas have trouble written all over them."*

196

"Shooters aren't really my thing," Al said, running his hand through his hair.

"Do you know someone?" Black Sandra persisted.

"Not really. I've never been in the market for one," Al said. "If I could help you I would."

Black Sandra took a long swig from her drink.

"Listen, why don't you just keep an eye out for this fella and when you find him just give me a call and I'll take care of him," Al said as he refilled her glass. "I'll give the bastard a good kicking and it's on the house."

"Thanks, but no thanks," Black Sandra said as she chinked her glass with Al's. "I want a shooter and I'm going to take care of him myself."

"Alright, but if you change your mind you'll find me in the Bell," Al said.

Al watched as she turned to leave. She was wearing a royal blue polka dot dress that ended just above the knee. With its narrowed hemline, Black Sandra took little steps while her hips swayed with a wiggle.

"Nice… very nice!" Al thought.

"I'll give you ten pounds each if you girls kiss," a short, middle-aged man wearing a chequered shirt and blue Levi jeans said, as he pulled a ten pound note out of his pocket.

"Okay," a short voluptuous brunette in heels said with a suggestive smile.

"It has to be a full-on snog and I'm talking tongues, the lot."

"I wouldn't do it any other way."

The brunette turned to the beautiful blonde with Joanna Lumley's Purdy from the Avengers hairstyle. She leaned forward slowly before gently parting her lips. The crowd watched as the blonde closed her eyes when their lips touched. The brunette kissed her like she wanted to be kissed, like no man had ever kissed her. The betting instigator's mouth dropped open as he witnessed their soft, moist, hot and erotic kiss. There was no battle of the tongues but a mutual seeking of closeness, to share one another's breath. It was one sensation, one timeless and passionate moment. A couple of the punters let out a silent gasp as the heat rose in the girl's cheeks while their tongues touched and became increasingly firmer, more determined and more curious about the heat that lay within, while chasing down that elusive liquid lightning.

The kiss finished and the girls slowly parted. It was almost silent in the crowded bar as *'Float On'* by the Floaters played.

"I think I want to be a lesbian," Timothy announced.

The bar erupted in cheers and raucous laughter as the two barmen ran back and forth refilling glasses and taking cash.

"Al," Mae said as he approached the bar with Harry the Poof.

Al nodded and refilled their glasses.

"This is a licence to print money," Mae said.

"This is just the first," Al thought as his smile stretched from ear to ear.

"Do you know what?" Mae said as he scanned all the people enjoying themselves. "If I had a bar it would be exclusively for gays."

"I like that," Harry the Poof said.

"The barmen would be totally naked," Mae said with a sigh. "They would need to be well hung and drop dead gorgeous."

"We could have cabaret music," Harry the Poof said.

"Where does 'we' come into it?" Mae said with a chuckle. "This was my fantasy."

Al spotted a punter at the end of the bar looking a little worse for wear.

"Brian," Al called. "Can you see that fella to the toilet? I think he's going to puke."

Brian nodded and sped off down the bar.

"We can't be having vomit on the carpet," Mae said with a chortle.

"I think those two love birds need to get a room," Harry the Poof said as he pointed out the betting guy and the brunette kissing passionately.

"They will," Mae said as he placed his drink on the bar. "That's Rhonda and the blonde she was kissing earlier, her friend and business partner Janet, and the whole girl on girl gig is their thing. That punter will be parting with big money for a threesome tonight."

"I'm stunned by these girls," Al said as he surveyed the room. "Away from their husbands and boyfriends they're really living it up!"

Chapter 21

Al's American Bar was in full swing when he left it to meet with Leaky back at the Bell in Pentonville Road.

"There you go," Al said as he put a tray of lager and whiskey chasers on the table.

"Cheers Al," Leaky said as he reached for a pint. "There's been a lot of talk about your new place."

"Really," Al said before taking a short sip from his lager.

"What is it... The American Bar?"

Al nodded.

"Apparently the place was wall to wall with girls and punters until the early hours," Leaky said.

"It was a good night," Al said.

"I'm pleased for you mate, but I'm not so sure that everyone in here will be," Leaky said. "Not without some kind of offering."

"Told to pass that on, were you?" Al said bluntly.

"No, of course not," Leaky said. "I've been using this place longer than you, Al, and I know how the politics can work."

Leaky leaned across the table and looked quickly from left to right.

"Dougie sees himself as number one and as far as he's concerned, he's entitled to a slice of anything outside the Bell," Leaky whispered.

"Well fuck him, fuck Heart Attack and fuck that silly cunt Big Jim Gibson too," Al muttered through gritted teeth.

"I'm just letting you know how I see it," Leaky said. "And just so you know, if it all kicks off, I fall firmly on the side of Al McIntosh... alright?"

"I had you down as a good bloke the first time I met you," Al said. "Everything will work out the way it's supposed to."

"I believe you," Leaky said before offering up his glass. "Cheers."

"Leaky. Can I have a word?"

Leaky looked up to see Lucy.

"Of course you can, sweetheart," Leaky said as he reached down and lifted a sports bag onto the table.

"Can I have some more of those fivers?" Lucy whispered.

"Sure. You can have a thousand fivers for four hundred pounds."

"That's about twelve and a half pence each," Al thought. *"I better make sure that these don't get passed in The American Bar."*

Lucy reached into her handbag, pulled out a roll of notes and counted off four hundred pounds.

"Nice business," Leaky said as he handed over ten bundles of one hundred five-pound notes. "Have fun."

Lucy flicked through the notes before placing the last bundle in her bag.

"Lucy," Leaky said just as she was about to turn and leave. "Tell your friends I only do lots of one thousand. When this lot has gone, I'll be happy to take orders."

Within a few minutes two girls approached the table.

"Leaky?"

"That would be me," Leaky said as he looked up at a beautiful redhead. "Oh my, you are a very pretty girl."

"Thank you," the girl said, blushing. "We're friends of Lucy and she said…"

"I know what she said," Leaky said. "One or two lots?"

"One each," the redhead said as she handed over a wad of twenty-pound notes.

Her friend, a blonde, also handed over four hundreds.

Leaky reached into his sports bag and counted out two lots of ten bundles.

"Girls," Leaky said. "Be sure to tell your friends. This little lot will be gone soon but I'm happy to take orders."

"I'm just going to have a slash," Al said as he slid past two new girls that arrived at their table with their handbags open.

Al passed by Dougie 'The Man' McKinnon's table.

"I won't tell you again SAS… Fuck off away from me!" Dougie yelled.

"I'm really sorry Dougie, I didn't mean anything by it," SAS whimpered.

"This is the fucking top table for men, real fucking hard men to talk business. It's not a place for you to talk your bollocks!" Dougie hissed, leaning over and intimidating SAS.

"If you tried that with me, I'd bite your fucking face off," Al thought as he pushed open the toilet door.

With one hand on the wall Al unzipped himself and allowed nature to take its course. Al raised his head when he heard the door open behind him. Once he shook himself dry a couple of times, he zipped himself up and walked over to the basin to wash his hands.

"McIntosh you flash cunt!" Big Jim Gibson shrieked. "Carol is with me so keep your fucking hands to yourself!"

Al turned swiftly and with the back of his hand slapped Big Jim Gibson viciously across the face.

"Who the fuck do you think you're talking to?" Al said as he clenched both fists and took a step closer to Big Jim. "I am not in the least bit interested in your bird so you better back off and talk to me with respect or I will fucking hurt you badly."

Big Jim visibly shrank as his shoulders fell and he lowered his head.

"Did you hear me?" Al said through gritted teeth, with his face just inches away from Big Jim's.

"Yeah... yes." Jim snivelled.

"Good, now fuck off!"

Al turned back to the basin and continued to wash his hands. Big Jim Gibson opened the door and left.

"Cheeky bastard," Al thought as he dried his hands on a paper towel. "I'm out of your league, son."

Al walked back through the pub. He saw his brother Brian was at the table. Leaky stood up and turned the sports bag upside down and began to shake it.

"Looks like you've had a result," Al said as he sat down.

"Sold the lot and took orders for twelve more lots, all in the time it took you syphon the python," Leaky said with a chuckle.

Lucy returned to the table.

"I'm sorry sweetheart, I'm all sold out," Leaky said.

"No, not that," Lucy said as she pulled out a chair and sat down.

"What's up?" Al said.

"I've just heard that Heart Attack was nicked today," Lucy mumbled.

"Really?" Al said as he leaned towards her.

"Yeah, by all accounts he pulled out a shooter in a bank down Greenwich way. The whole thing went tits up because there were three plain clothes old bill waiting for him," Lucy said. "I thought you'd want to know Al."

"Thank you, sweetheart," Leaky said.

"Yeah, cheers Lucy," Al said. "That's interesting...very interesting."

"That explains Dougie getting pissed off with SAS," Al thought.

"You know what this means, don't you?" Leaky said. "The empire is crumbling."

"Time to take over then," Brian said as he patted the table firmly with the palm of his hand.

Al turned to face Brian and then Leaky.

"We wait and let the thing crumble," Al said with a smirk. "I have my own plans."

"I'm with you," Brian said.

"Me too," Leaky said.

The three friends drank and chatted until Large William entered the pub.

"Hello mate," Al said as he stood and shook Large William's hand.

"That booze alright for you?" Large William said.

"It's going down a treat," Al said. "I might need some more."

"No problem," Large William said as he put his half full glass of lager on the table. "Just let me know, or I'll let you know if something comes up in the meantime."

"Will do," Al said.

"Anyway, it wasn't really about business that I came here to talk to you," Large William said. "I wanted to ask you a favour."

"One minute," Al said as he waved SAS over.

"You want me, Al?" SAS said.

"Yes mate, will you do us all a favour?" Al said.

"Yeah, of course," SAS said with huge smile.

Al handed him a twenty-pound note.

"Can you get another round of lagers and whiskey chasers for everyone and get yourself the same?"

"Sure, Al," SAS said enthusiastically.

"Sorry William, how can I help?" Al said as he turned back to Large William.

"He seems eager to please," Large William said with a smile.

"He's harmless," Al said.

"Al, I've got to go to Ireland to a friend's wake."

"Okay," Al said.

"I'm not comfortable leaving my wife and our pub without some kind of protection," Large William said.

"Do you know, I forgot that you even have a pub," Al said with a chortle.

"Well, you have to have something on record to pay a bit of tax. Besides its perfect for passing on some of our own gear," Large William said.

"No problem at all," Al said as reached over and patted Large William on the upper arm. "Consider it done."

"We don't get much aggravation all things considered, but with this sudden influx of working girls and the new punters on the scene you never know," Large William said. "It's better to be safe than sorry."

"I'll pop around tomorrow to scope the place out," Al said.

"I may be away seven or ten days," Large William said.

"That's alright," Al said.

"I'll sort you out for it," Large William said.

"Leave it out, we're friends," Al said.

"Then we'll sort something on that next load."

"I'm happy to do it," Al said. "You'd do it for me, wouldn't you?"

"In a heartbeat, mate."

SAS put the tray on the table, stood back and pulled his shoulders back as if standing to attention.

"Are we done with business?" Al said as he turned to face all those at the table.

Once everyone confirmed, Al invited SAS to join them.

***

It was just after midnight when Al and Brian returned to the squat in Gloucester Drive carrying a bucket of KFC chicken. Al handed the bucket to Brian and then pushed the key into the lock and opened the front door. The light was on in the front room, and he heard voices. Al opened the door from the hallway into the lounge and saw his brother Wullie sitting on the sofa chatting to Sandy.

"Wullie," Al said as he handed the KFC bucket to Sandy. "What are you doing down here?"

"Hello Al, Brian... Have you seen Mammy?"

206

Al sat down on the armchair. He found himself sobering up.

"No, not in a while," said Al.

"Have you still got that shotgun and cattle prod?" Brian asked as he sat on the other armchair.

"Yes of course," Wullie said as he pointed at a long black sports bag by the fireplace. "I am going to kill her, Al."

Al didn't reply, he just raised his eyebrows.

"Jesus talks to me," Wullie said. "Every night my friend Jesus tells me what a bitch Mammy was to me and how she deserves to die. Jesus told me Al, he told me I have to kill her."

Al looked over at the shocked expression on Sandy's face.

"Mammy was far from perfect," Al said.

"Mammy was evil Al," Wullie said, raising his eyes to the ceiling. "That's why Jesus told me to kill her, and I have to do it soon."

"Would you like some chicken?" Sandy asked, offering Wullie the bucket.

"You're a very nice lady," Wullie said, shaking his head. "I'm pleased that you and my brother Brian are together."

Sandy offered the bucket and a paper towel to Brian.

"You should get a nice girl like Sandy, Al," Wullie said.

"Maybe I will one day," Al said. "For right now I'm happy as I am."

"You have got worse since the last time I saw you," Al thought. *"I could batter you into next week for what you did to my dog. I could really fucking hurt you, Wullie, but I gave my word to Brian. You have no idea how hard it is for me to sit here like everything between us is hunky dory when images of what you did to my dog come into my head."*

207

Chapter 22

With the American Bar rocking until the early hours every night, Al rolled out the business model into another squat. He had a team of lads come in and gut the place, install a bar, curtains, carpets and had it painted crimson and cream throughout. Al called the Speeler 'Raffles'.

Large William had a truck load of alcohol delivered on the morning he was due to fly out to Ireland for the wake. A few of the customers at the American Bar had suggested that Al introduce some kind of simple food. At first Al considered burgers and chips but was put off by the idea of the smell in the bar. While out, he stopped at a bakery. There were a range of simple cheese and pickle, ham and pickle, and egg mayonnaise rolls at thirty pence each. When he shared his food idea with Brian and Sandra she immediately leapt on the opportunity and volunteered to buy all the ingredients and make up a large batch of rolls wrapped in cellophane. Along with Al's premium price strategy, the rolls were priced at three pounds each. Once again, the girls were put on a healthy commission for encouraging their punters to buy the rolls.

The opening night was a huge success with new faces all brought in by the working girls. Al loved the 'everybody earns' business model. It was sustainable and repeatable. Al had met with suppliers of slot machines and had two installed in The American Bar and another two at Raffles. Al was stunned when he witnessed the two machines in the American Bar were being fed coins non-stop, with a queue waiting to play from the moment the bar opened until the very early hours of the morning. They kept a metal fire bucket under the bar filled with coins so they could change up the customer's notes.

'September,' by Earth Wind & Fire was playing when Al joined Leaky at his table for a drink.

"I think I may prefer this place to the Bell," Leaky said as he popped two Black Bombers into his mouth.

"Between here and The American Bar we have quite a few of their regulars anyway," Al said.

"Leaky, do you have any more," Lucy said, lowering her voice. "Fivers?"

Leaky reached down and put his black sports bag on his lap.

"How many do you need?" Leaky said as he pulled out several bundles of freshly printed fivers.

"Just the usual amount," Lucy said as she handed over four hundred pounds.

"Can you do me a favour?" Leaky asked as he leaned over the table and grinned.

"Not if it's got anything to do with that huge dildo again," Lucy grimaced as she stepped back. "You're a nice guy and I like you, but that thing and what you want to do with it just isn't normal."

"I think she must be talking about the Empire State Building," Leaky said as he turned to Al and chuckled.

Leaky turned back to Lucy.

"You are safe from the Empire," Leaky said. "I wanted you to tell all your friends that I am now in the very fortunate position of being able to supply driving licences, passports, birth certificates and cheque books.

"Oh, okay," Lucy said with a look of relief.

"Lucy, darling, I am open for orders," Leaky said.

Al poured Leaky a whiskey.

"To good business," Al said.

"I can drink to that," Leaky said as they chinked glasses.

"Talking about good business," Leaky said as he turned to face Al. "Dougie 'The Man' McKinnon has got the right hump with you. He's pissed off with hearing Al this and Al that and it doesn't help with SAS relaying his embellished version of what happened at the council building in Essex Road to anyone who will listen."

Al shrugged his shoulders and took a sip of his drink.

"I probably already know the answer to this," Leaky said as he moved his chair closer to Al. "Would you consider giving him something. I don't know, maybe a hundred quid a week so his pride stays intact?"

Al shook his head.

"Not a bean," Al replied calmly.

"I don't give a flying fuck about Dougie 'The Man' McKinnon," Al thought, remaining calm and unperturbed. *"We will come to blows sooner or later and when it happens, I'll fucking hurt him good and proper and make it very public. When the time is right for me, he will get what's coming."*

"Leaky?"

Al looked up to see two smartly dressed lads in their mid-twenties. They wore smart shirts, trousers and polished shoes.

"Are these old bill?" Al thought as he looked them up and down.

"Bootsie, Smudge, good to see you lads," Leaky said as he motioned them to sit down.

"This is an interesting place," Bootsie said.

"I'm not sure I've ever seen so much available skirt in one place," Smudge said as he turned to scan the room.

'One Nation Under a Groove,' by Funkadelic began to play.

"This is my friend Al, Al McIntosh, and Raffles is one of his Speelers," Leaky said.

Al shook hands with them both.

"Bootsie, mate we need to come to this part of town more often," Smudge said as he watched a leggy blonde wearing a white pleated mini dress and heels walk past him. "What are the best nights?"

Al gave them the address of the American Bar and confirmed that both Speelers were busy and wall to wall with pretty, available, working girls every night of the week.

"First and foremost, your fivers have gone down a storm in South London," Smudge said. "So we want more, twice the amount as last time."

"These are my biggest customers," Leaky said with a wink to Al before turning back to Smudge. "No problem. I need a few days."

"What is it you have for us?" Smudge asked.

Leaky reached into his black holdall and put a cheque book on the table.

"Check it out lads, it's perfect," Leaky said triumphantly.

Smudge flicked through the cheque book and then passed it over to Bootsie.

"It looks good," Smudge said as he put it back on the table. "How much and how many have you got?"

"Each of those cheques is good for fifty pounds in cash or goods, so I'm asking a very reasonable five pounds per cheque. Twenty cheques in each book is a hundred quid for me and a thousand pounds to you," Leaky said as he pushed the cheque book a couple of inches closer to Smudge.

"That sounds fair," Smudge said. "How many do you have?

Leaky smiled.

"I have twelve books with me and over a hundred stashed away," Leaky said.

Al motioned the barman to bring over a bottle of whiskey and two additional glasses.

Smudge looked at Bootsie, smiled and then turned back to Leaky.

"We'll have all twelve books," Smudge said as he reached into his pocket and produced a thick wad of twenty-pound notes.

"Leaky slid the twelve books across the table and put the twelve hundred pounds into his sports bag.

"I'd like to talk to you about the other cheque books," Smudge said. "We'll have these cashed up within a week or so in and around South London. We'll take everything you've got on the understanding that you don't roll them out to other firms in volume. I'm not concerned about a book or two here and there, but we want exclusivity to any big numbers."

"They're all yours," Leaky said.

"What about Euro-Cheque Books?" Bootsie said.

"I'm working on those," Leaky said as he poured both Smudge and Bootsie a glass of neat whiskey. "Plus, I can throw in a passport or two for the right kind of volumes."

"We're definitely interested in those too," Smudge said as he raised his glass.

"They'll be yours," Leaky said confidently.

"Right, with business out of the way, I think me and my mate here will circulate amongst the girls," Smudge said. "This is a nice place you have here, Al."

Al left Leaky to selling his five-pound notes to the working girls and joined Mae West and Harry the Poof.

'Can You Feel the Force' by The Real Thing boomed out of the speakers while a city gent pranced around with his shirt unbuttoned to the waist wearing his bowler hat and holding a ten-inch dildo, mock sword fighting with one of the girls.

"You've done it again," Mae said.

"I just like everybody to earn and have a good time," Al said.

"You do know that Dougie 'The Man' McKinnon is pissed with you, right?" Mae said.

"Apparently," Al said as he rolled his eyes and then turned to watch the city gent leaping around, calling out that he was Luke Skywalker, and the girl was Darth Vader.

"That's Al," Mae West said as he turned to Harry the Poof. "He doesn't give a fuck."

"Harry and I have been talking," Mae said with a hint of seriousness in his voice.

"Go on," Al said.

"We've been thinking about opening a Speeler exclusive to gay people," Mae said.

"Yeah, you mentioned something like that at the American Bar's opening night," Al said.

"Well that was a kind of fantasy, but the more Harry and I talked about it and seeing what you've done, the more we thought we'd like to give it a go ourselves," Mae said.

"That sounds like a great idea, Mae," Al said.

"Between us we have just about everything we need to get things going except a place," Mae said.

Al hesitated for a moment and then smiled.

"I've been looking around for my next Speeler and I have found somewhere that is perfect," Al said. "I've already been in, sorted the electric and changed all the locks, so it's ready to go. It's yours."

"Pardon?" Mae said.

"Yeah, you heard right," Al said. "I have the perfect place and it's yours."

"Okay… what do you want?" Harry the Poof said cautiously.

"Nothing, you're my friends and I'd love to see you both with your own gay Speeler," Al said as he patted Mae on his arm. "I'll go one step further and let you have some of my booze at cost to get you on your feet."

"You would do that for me?" Mae said rubbing his eye.

"I haven't forgotten how, when I was cold and starving, it was you and Jean Harlow that took me in, bought me fish and chips and got me a place to stay. This is the very least that I could do for a friend," Al said.

"We better have a drink to celebrate the opening of Raffles, and to Mae and I opening our own gay Speeler," Harry the Poof said.

"Talking about drink," Al said as he looked down at his watch. "I promised to pay a visit to Large William's pub to make sure the natives aren't getting restless."

***

Al stepped into Large William's boozer and quickly scanned the room before going over to the bar and ordering a drink.

"Hello Dot, I'm Al McIntosh," Al said as the landlady handed him a pint of lager.

Dot was in her mid-thirties. She had a slim, hourglass figure with a tapered waist. Her flawless bronze complexion disguised a decade of pub management. Dot had an elegant nose and wore a blush pink lipstick. Her most striking feature was her long black vulcanite hair that toppled over her shoulders.

"Large William asked me to pop in from time to time," Al said as he placed a pound note on the bar.

"I don't know why he does things like this," Dot said as she scooped up the note and put it in the till. "I had eight years with him locked away and I did just fine with this lot."

"I suppose I'm a kind of insurance," Al said. "You hope you'll never need it, but it's there for if you do."

"How did you meet Large William?" Dot said as she began to wipe down the bar with a black cloth.

"We met and became good friends in Pentonville," Al said.

"So you do protection?"

"I have a few bits and pieces on the go and every so often I'll help out a friend if needed," Al said as he took his first sip of the pint.

"I'd like him to go straight," Dot said with a sigh. "It's not like the pub doesn't make us a good living. I'm convinced that he just gets off on the buzz of working with his school mates. I love my husband, Al, and I don't want him to go back inside again. I couldn't bear it."

"I'm not sure what I should be saying to this," Al thought as he smiled weakly. *"Large William has a good, loyal, wife who clearly loves him and just wants him by her side. I hope I find what Large William has in a relationship one day.*

The pub door slammed open. Al turned to watch six men enter. They were led by a tall skinny guy with mousey brown hair.

Probably in his mid-forties. Al couldn't help but notice the guy had a huge, inflamed nose with lumpy skin and broken blood vessels.

"Hello, what have we here?" Al thought as he put his lager down on the bar.

"Do you know these guys?" Al whispered.

Dot nodded her head.

"They call him the 'Nose'."

"I ain't fucking surprised with a hooter like that," Al thought.

"No one calls him that to his face," Dot said. "He's gone to Harley Street and had all sorts of tests. Cost him a fortune by all accounts, but they're stumped. His nose isn't like that all the time. It's a condition that just comes and goes. The other lads are all publicans. He leads a kind of unofficial consortium to control beer prices."

"Hello Dot, is Large William around?" the Nose said.

"No, he's in Ireland attending a wake," Dot said as she reached for a straight glass and began to pour him a drink."

"Make that five pints and a vodka and tonic," the Nose said before turning around and scanning the pub.

Al nursed his pint and watched the Nose collect the tray and take the drinks to a table.

"He didn't pay," Al said.

Dot shook her head.

"It's alright, Al. He comes in here to push his weight about once a week. It's normally on a Tuesday with a few of the publicans. They have a few drinks and then leave."

"Is Large William alright with him not paying?"

Dot nodded her head.

"It's just part of doing business here," Dot said.

"As long as you're sure, because I can make them pay for those drinks," Al said as he turned towards their table. "It won't be a problem."

Al watched the Nose and his publican friends chatting, laughing and sinking one free drink after another.

"I have a plan coming together," Al thought as he watched them carefully. *"This is going to work well and fit in with my bigger ambitions*

***

Al visited Large William's pub every night. When Tuesday arrived, Al was sitting on the bar stool nursing his pint. Right on time the Nose arrived. The pub door, true to form, slammed open and this time eight publicans entered. They pushed two tables together while the Nose demanded the free drinks.

Al had a plan, and it was coming together perfectly.

The publicans drank their free drinks, chatted and became quite animated when the fourth round of free drinks arrived at their table.

"Why don't you cunts keep your fucking noise down!"

The Nose and the publicans looked up to see a stocky looking thug in jeans, white polo shirt and a black leather bomber jacket.

"I can't hear myself think with the fucking racket you lot are making," the thug said as he staggered a little and then recovered.

"Oh fucking hell!" Dot hissed.

The Nose put his beer on the table and shot up with both fists clenched.

The thug reached into his leather jacket and pulled out a shooter.

There were several gasps from around the pub. The Nose unclenched his fists and held his hands up in the air.

"I'll blow your fucking head off!" the thug said as he waved the gun around.

Al calmly stepped off the bar stool and walked over towards the armed thug.

"What, you want some?" the drunken thug said as turned sharply and pointed the gun at Al.

Al continued to walk towards the thug and then lurched forward and grabbed the weapon.

The thug had been disarmed.

"Come on," Al said calmly. "You've had a couple of drinks too many. It's time to get yourself off home."

The thug looked at Al and then down at the floor.

"Yeah, sorry about that."

"I'm keeping this," Al said as he held up the shooter. "But I do expect you to be in here tomorrow, sober, to apologise to Dot."

"Yeah, yeah alright," the thug said as he was led to the pub door and then out into the street.

Once the pub door closed and they were outside in the street, the thug looked up at Al.

"How did I do?" the thug whispered.

"Perfect... your Oscar for best actor is in the post," Al said with a chuckle.

Chapter 23

Al had decided that afternoon that he would confront Dougie 'The Man' McKinnon before beating seven kinds of shit out of him in a very public display of savage violence to cement his new position. Al concluded that the old-school 1960's gangster had no place in the 1970's underworld.

The Bell was heaving with regulars, new girls and punters looking for a good time. Brian returned to the table with a tray of drinks.

"I had a really good day today," Sandy said before lighting her cigarette.

"Yeah? What did you do?" Al said before turning to scan the bar for Dougie 'The Man' McKinnon.

"I decided that I would take a good look around London," Sandy said as she puffed on her cigarette. "I left the motorbike and used the underground. My first stop was Soho."

"I know that place well," Al said with a broad smile.

"It was absolutely crammed. Packed with porn shops, brothels and strip clubs. I know that the streets come alive with working girls at night," Sandy said as she stubbed out her cigarette, "But the prostitutes were everywhere in broad daylight asking men if they wanted a nice girl. One pretty little thing actually propositioned me."

Both Al and Brian turned slowly to face Sandy with their mouths slightly ajar.

"And?" Brian said finally.

"And nothing Brian," Sandy said as she slapped him playfully on his arm.

"I stopped for a coffee and heard two men talking about the topless waitress bar they had gone into. They paid an entrance fee to get into the hallway, and then another fee because they were not members of the 'private club'. Then, and this did make me chuckle, they were charged another fee to sit down at the bar and have a drink with a topless waitress. I think it would be fair to say that they felt like they'd been ripped off."

"That's Soho," Al said.

"I was surprised by how many entrance doorways had the word 'MODEL' written on a fluorescent card and there were red lights glowing in the rooms. You can easily imagine how some country bumpkin, farmer type, could find himself in big trouble. I did see one building, I think it must have been a hostel, with old women sitting outside. Their hair was long, unkempt and greasy. A couple of the street prostitutes were happily chatting to them," Sandy said.

"Soho is not for everyone," Brian said.

"There's a lot of money to be made there," Al said.

"I had a walk down to Foyle's Bookshop. I couldn't believe that you could dedicate seven whole floors to the sale of books."

"Did you buy anything?" Al asked as he looked around the bar for the second time.

"I did actually. I heard these two schoolgirls talking about *'Catcher in the Rye'* by JD Salinger. They seemed very excited by the read so I bought a copy.

"I've heard about that," Al said as he turned back to face Sandy. "It's pretty good by all accounts."

"I took a walk down to the Kings Road, Chelsea, and it was lined from top to bottom with small boutique shops with the most amazing clothes," Sandy said. "Not that I would wear them, but they were something else."

220

"You should treat yourself," Brian said.

"Really?" Sandy said as she tilted her head to one side. "Could you really see me in a short paisley dress riding my bike?"

Brian looked up briefly.

"Actually, I can visualise that and it looks pretty damn good."

"In your dreams," Sandy said. "This girl is a biker through and through."

Sandy lit another cigarette.

"Ladbroke Grove, Notting Hill and Clapham were pretty run-down impoverished neighbourhoods," Sandy said. "Regardless of skin colour, poor areas are the same all over."

"That's true," Al said before looking over at the door.

"I did like Tottenham Court Road," Sandy said, her eyes lighting up. "There were so many hi-fi shops. I took a look around a couple and the shop assistants were just like those back in Glasgow... rude and unhelpful."

"If you want a particular hi-fi system Sandy, there's a team of shop lifters in here that will get just about anything you want at half the retail price," Al said.

"No. I'm alright, thanks," Sandy said as she drew heavily on her cigarette. "I can definitely see why people gravitate towards London."

"That's because it's the capital of the world," Leaky said as he put his drink on the table.

"Hello mate," Al said as he motioned for him to join them.

"Nasty business in here last night," Baldy said. "Fucking diabolical in my view."

Chris Knight was known by all as Baldy in the Bell pub because he had lost all his hair prematurely. He was hypersensitive about the condition and went to great lengths to explain that his Harley Street doctors had assured him it was a temporary condition and that his hair would grow back. Whilst Baldy was an easy-going guy, he became extremely irritated and violent when challenged over his hair loss condition.

"What was?" Al said.

"That Dougie 'The Man' McKinnon is right out of fucking order in my opinion," Baldy said firmly.

"Well come on then, what happened?" Al said as he turned to face Baldy.

"Dougie has this mate, Smithy, who was in here recruiting for men to go out to Rhodesia. He was going from table to table glamorising the war and saying how he had been killing men and getting paid big money for it. I caught a glimpse of this photo with some bastard's severed head being held up by Smithy and a bunch of Rhodesian soldiers. They were all laughing. Fucking sick," Baldy said.

"Did anyone we know sign up to go?" Al said.

Baldy shook his head and closed his eyes.

"SAS was pissed, and he was lapping up everything Smithy was saying, so he volunteered. Well, when Smithy announced to the pub that there was a real hard man in the pub Dougie fucking hit the roof," Baldy said. "He has taken it as a personal insult that SAS has even gone over and spoken to Smithy. I reckon he must have thought that he'd lost some kind of face in front of his mate and SAS was the root cause of all his embarrassment. Dougie has leapt up, pulled out this fucking claw hammer and proceeded to beat the shit out of SAS."

"That is well out of order!" Brian said.

"SAS is harmless," Al said. "Everyone knows he hasn't served a day in the army."

"He was left in a right state, Al," Baldy said. "The poor bastard was battered senseless and covered in blood. I don't think anyone in here was happy about it. The ambulance took about ten minutes and SAS was still out cold. To be honest with you at one point I thought he was dead."

"You're a fucking bully Dougie," Al thought as he grimaced. *"I despise who and what you are. You're a schoolboy ruffian; nothing more and nothing less. I was going to hurt you tonight but now I'm going to batter you so bad you'll never show your face around here again!"*

"The old bill arrived with the ambulance, and they nicked Dougie," Baldy said. "Cuffed him and took him away. To be honest, for the first time in my life I nearly cheered to see someone get nicked and I think, from people's expressions in here, they were thinking the same thing."

"So that's Heart Attack and Dougie 'The Man' McKinnon both banged up, which leaves that spineless wanker Big Jim Gibson. Now is the time!" Al thought.

"We should have a whip round for SAS," Baldy said as pulled a wad of notes out of his pocket.

"I'll put a hundred quid in," Al said.

"Me too," Brian said.

"I thought he was alright," Sandy said as she handed over five twenty-pound notes.

Baldy took their money and proceeded to go from table to table collecting a whip round for SAS. Al watched as every one of the regulars, without exception, made a contribution.

"Mr McIntosh."

A woman in her early thirties stood in front of Al's table. Her eyes were red and sore. She appeared to have been crying.

"It's Al, how can I help you?" Al said as he turned his chair to face her. "Can I get you a drink?"

"No, no drink, thank you," the woman said. "I'm Tammy White. I think you know my husband, Don."

"The name rings a bell," Al said.

"Don was in court last week on a robbery charge," Tammy said. "We all expected him to walk away as the evidence against him was circumstantial at best. He got five years."

"I'm really sorry to hear that Tammy," Al said. "This must be a very difficult time for you."

Tammy nodded and began to sniffle.

"I really don't like to be coming in here like this, but with three young children and Don away, we are struggling to make ends meet. The cupboards are empty, and my children are hungry, and I just didn't know what else to do," Tammy said as the tears streamed down her face.

"You did exactly the right thing," Al said as he motioned a woman known as Kim over to the table.

Kim Carr was a professional shoplifter. She specialised in taking high value food from supermarkets. Day in and day out she would take a trolley and fill it to the brim with steak, chickens, lamb, pork, bacon and sausages and then sell it at half price at the Bell.

"You wanted me, Al?" Kim said.

"Yeah, what have you got for sale?"

"I've just done a full day's shop, so I've pretty much got all my usual haul," Kim said with a quizzical expression.

"Do you know Don White?"

Kim nodded.

"This is his wife, Tammy," Al said as he pointed to Tammy. "Don will be away for a while."

"Okay," Kim said as she acknowledged Tammy.

"How much for everything you have?" Al said.

"There's a lot there, Al," Kim said. "It would normally bring me one hundred and thirty maybe one hundred and forty quid. Is this for Tammy?"

Al reached into his pocket and produced a large wad of cash.

"It is. How much?"

"One hundred pounds for you," Kim said with a smile.

Al counted out one hundred pounds and handed it to Kim and then peeled off another hundred pounds and handed it to Tammy.

"Thank you, thank you so much," Tammy said, floods of tears rolling down her cheeks.

"Kim, can you give Tammy a lift home and help her in with the goods?"

"Of course," Kim said with a warm smile. "Come on Tammy let's get you home."

Al checked his wad of notes before putting them back in his pocket.

"Did you know Don?" Al asked as he turned to Brian.

"I might have spoken to him a couple of times," Brian said as he shrugged his shoulders.

"Hold up," Al muttered to himself as the pub door opened and in stepped the 'Nose', closely followed by several of the publicans he recognised from his friend, Large William's pub.

One of his followers went to the bar while the others followed the Nose to Al's table.

"Would you mind if we joined you?" the Nose asked as the publicans surrounded the table.

Al turned to Brian and Sandy.

"Would you mind giving us a few minutes," Al said.

"It's all coming together," Al thought as he invited them to sit down.

Brian looked at the 'Nose' and then made eye contact with each and every one of the publicans before rising to his feet.

"We'll be at the bar if you need me," Brian said, maintaining constant eye contact with the largest of the publicans.

The Nose pulled out a chair and sat down opposite Al.

"We saw what you did to that nutcase with the gun the other night and we've been asking around about you, Al," the Nose said. "What we witnessed was a man that defused an extremely dangerous situation quickly and effectively so that customers continued to enjoy their time out and spend money."

"Large William is a good friend, and I was happy to help," Al said.

"I represent fifteen pubs," the Nose said as he sat back in his chair. "We operate a kind of co-operative, and we would like you to protect all of our pubs. Can you do that?"

Al hesitated for a moment and then leaned over the table.

"I can protect all your pubs, that isn't a problem. That doesn't mean that I'll always be there, but you will have a number and when you call you can be sure that whatever the size of your problem, it will be dealt with," Al said. "I want two hundred pounds per week per pub and I want you to put me down in the books as a 'bouncer'. I want everything legal and above board. This is not protection money, okay?"

The Nose turned to his fellow publicans and then turned back to Al and nodded.

"In addition," Al said as he homed in on the Nose. "I will be taking ten percent of everything sold in your pubs. That's robberies, shoplifting, stolen goods, absolutely everything. Do we have an agreement?"

The Nose held out his hand across the table for Al to shake.

"The plan has gone like bloody clock work," Al thought as he said goodbye to the Nose. *"Two hundred quid per pub and fifteen of them, that's three thousand pounds a week, all legal and above board plus ten per-cent of everything that moves inside. With all that's coming in now from the Speelers, this is one extremely sweet deal. You were lucky to have been nicked when you were, Dougie 'The Man' McKinnon, because with this kind of money at stake it would have spelt your end."*

Chapter 24

Leaky was sat with Bootsie and Smudge when Al arrived at the Bell.

"The place is crawling with Newcastle United fans," Al said as he surveyed the pub. "There must be a game on somewhere."

"They're playing the rent boys down at Stamford Bridge," Smudge said as he handed a thick pile of notes to Leaky.

"Rent boys?" Al said as he sat down.

"Yeah, most people call Chelsea the 'Rent Boys'. They do have a firm of lads who call themselves the 'Head Hunters' but to us they're just the 'Rent Boys'," Smudge said as he put several thick piles of cheque books into his sports bag.

"You seem to know a lot about it," Al said.

"We're from Bermondsey so we're indoctrinated from birth," Smudge said with a chuckle.

"I wouldn't have it any other way," Bootsie said, rising to his feet. "Al, what you having?"

"Cheers, I'll have a lager," Al said before turning to Leaky. "Is business good?"

Leaky patted the inside pocket of his jacket and smiled.

"My friends from Millwall here have taken everything I've got, so business is extremely good," Leaky said.

"Sorry mate!"

A small bunch of Newcastle fans passed by the table and one lad bumped into the back of Al's chair.

"No problem," Al said.

"Most of these are just 'scarfers'," Smudge said as he reached for his pint. "They're just your everyday fans who follow their team. Harmless until it kicks off and then they all think they're top boys."

"The whole of Kings Cross is crawling with them," Al said as he turned to look around the Bell for the second time. "It's good for business though."

"With so many old bill at the games now it makes it difficult plotting up for a drink near the ground after the game," Smudge said. "Besides, most hardcore Chelsea fans don't even come from Chelsea so they would have pissed off back to Mitcham, Sutton and Rose Hill. So with Kings Cross having a train to Newcastle... They're here on your manor Al."

"As long as they keep spending, I'm happy," Al said as Bootsie put a tray of lager on the table.

"Here," Bootsie muttered to Smudge as he sat back down. "Over there in the corner."

Smudge turned to look and then turned back.

"Problem?" Al asked.

"Probably not," Bootsie said before taking a sip from his glass. "The lads in the far corner by the pool table, dressed in Fred Perry polo shirts, smart Farah trousers and loafers."

Al turned casually towards the table of lads.

"They're part of the Toon Army," Bootsie said. "I recognise a couple of them."

"What the fuck is a Toon Army?" Leaky said.

"Almost every football team has at least one if not two hooligan firms. Newcastle has a group of lads called the 'Toon Army'. The St James Park ground is in the town centre and by all accounts that's how their name came about. You know we call it town, well up North it's 'toon'," Bootsie said as he peered over his pint. "Chelsea have the Head Hunters, West Ham the ICF - Inter City Firm, Tottenham are the Yids and Birmingham are the Zulu's. There are hundreds of naughty firms all over the UK waiting anxiously for the weekend so they can have a tear up."

"The most notorious of all is Millwall's F-Troop," Smudge announced with a broad smile.

"It all sounds like bollocks to me," Al thought as he reached for his pint.

One drunken fan climbed up onto a chair, raised his glass and began to sing:

'We love Newcastle, we do

We love Newcastle, we do

We love Newcastle, we do

Oh, Newcastle we love you!'

Fans from all around the pub joined and sang at the top of their voices.

"Newcastle is a Northern shit hole," Bootsie said.

"Yeah, but then again, so is Bermondsey," Smudge said with a raucous laugh.

"There are a lot of new girls in here," Leaky said as he watched a small group of attractive young girls walk over towards the bar.

"They're still arriving by the train load from all over," Al said as he looked over at the door. "The Speelers are jam packed every night until the early hours."

Black Sandra had just entered the pub. Al couldn't help but notice that she looked flustered.

230

"Excuse me lads," Al said as he got up and excused himself.

"Hey, are you alright?" Al said as he approached Black Sandra at the bar.

Al motioned the barman to bring over two whiskeys.

"Oh, hello darling, yeah, I suppose so," Black Sandra said as she turned to face Al.

"Come on, tell me all about it." Al said with a sympathetic smile.

Black Sandra hesitated for a few moments and then took a sip of her drink.

"I share a squat with a couple of girls in Kings Cross. One of the girls, Donna, is pregnant... almost eight months gone. This morning we've had a couple of debt collectors turn up and they forced their way in and started knocking shit off the shelves. Big brave fuckers when it comes to three girls. Donna owes, but she doesn't have a pot to piss in, Al, and the baby is just about due. The boyfriend is long gone and unlikely to be back on the scene. We tried, and I mean really tried to explain the situation, but they were having none of it. One of the men, a fucking ginger nut with a matching moustache opened the window and threw our television out onto the pavement. I paid for that television, and I was pissed, extremely pissed, but that ugly ginger bastard just laughed and said that if we didn't want to see them again, we have to settle her debt," Black Sandra said, and then swallowed the last of her whiskey.

"Listen," Al said as he placed his hand on her shoulder. "The next time these debt collectors turn up I want you to give me a ring here at the Bell. I will come and I will take care of it."

"Why... why would you get involved?" Black Sandra said as she shrugged her shoulders.

"Number one I don't like bully boys," Al said firmly. "Secondly, we're friends and helping out is the kind of thing that friends do, right?"

"Friends," Black Sandra said with a quizzical smile.

"Yeah, friends," Al said as he nodded his head slowly.

"You are a stunning woman," Al thought.

"Al, you alright?"

It was Brian, Al's brother.

"You know... Sandra, don't you?" Al said.

"It's Black Sandra. Everyone calls me Black Sandra, darling."

Al ordered a round of drinks and returned to the table with Black Sandra and Brian.

"Where's Sandy?" Al said as he handed out the drinks.

"She's working," Brian said with a wink.

Back in the corner the Newcastle fan was back on the chair waving his pint around again.

'Oh, when the Mags

Go marching in

Oh, when the Mags go marching in

I want to be in that number

Oh, when the Mags go marching in.'

There were an increasing number of fans in and around the pub and all were singing along to the Newcastle Magpies song.

"Lively lot," Brian said in an almost dismissive tone.

'We are the Geordies! The Geordie Boot Boys!

For we are mental! For we are mad!

For we're the loyalist football supporters!

The world has ever seen!'

'Fucking Geordie maggots," Bootsie muttered.

"I think the strip show is about to start," Leaky said as he pulled his chair around.

A young girl with long, curly ebony black hair that had been styled into a chignon with a new HB pencil placed through its centre stepped out of the ladies' toilets. She wore a crisp white collared blouse with a jet-black pencil skirt, black seamed stockings and stiletto heels. The stripper stopped and put her hands on her hips while she looked around at her drunken, laddish audience. She then strutted towards the middle of the bar.

Al couldn't help but notice her sensuous walk.

"My name is Shaz, and I'm about to perform a show for you. Let me be very clear that I am in complete control. I'm trusting all you nice Geordie boys to sit and behave," Shaz said before turning and waving to the barman.

'Kashmir,' by Led Zeppelin pounded through the pub's speaker system.

Shaz began to dance. She moved her hips sensuously in a slow figure of eight. She approached a tall teenage lad who wore a black and white scarf around his neck. While still circling her hips, she extended her middle finger and lifted the lad's chin.

"Whoo hoo!" yelled the lads as Shaz inched towards him. She parted her ruby red lips as if she was about to kiss him and then lightly pushed his head back.

"Whaaaa!" the laddish audience cried.

Shaz swivelled around and continued her sensuous dance. She reached up with Aphrodite-red manicured fingernails and slowly undid a button on her blouse. Shaz turned leisurely, smiled seductively, and undid two more buttons before raising her shoulders slightly so that the blouse slid down a little, exposing her shoulder.

"Have it!" one lad yelled while another gasped silently.

Shaz extracted both arms from the sleeves and then turned to face her audience, but at the same time she expertly moved the blouse so that it covered her black lace bra. She then let it slowly drop to the floor.

"Fucking yes!" one lad cried.

Shaz was in complete control. All eyes, male and female, were on her as she arched her back, unzipped, and then allowed her pencil skirt to fall in one fluid motion.

The pub erupted in cheers and strident applause as her black seamed stockings, suspenders and red silky panties were exposed.

Shaz slipped her stiletto heels off effortlessly before placing her right leg on a chair. She ran her tongue enticingly over her lips before unhooking her stocking. As the audience gasped, she ran her hand slowly down her leg and then back up again before rolling her stocking off and letting it fall to the ground.

"I want to meet her," Leaky whispered.

"We all fucking do!" Smudge whispered.

With both stockings on the floor Shaz continued to dance and gyrate her hips into a figure of eight movement.

One lad began to sing and within seconds every Newcastle United supporter joined him.

'Get your tits out

Get your tits out

Get your tits out for the boys

Get your tits out for the boys!'

Shaz smiled, unclipped her black lace bra and allowed her perky, pert, breasts to fall free.

"Yes!" the lads cried out as the record came to a stop and she reached down and collected her garments.

The lads cheered and clapped as she skipped off back into the ladies' toilets.

"I think the strippers have definitely brought in more punters," Leaky said.

"Sex sells," Black Sandra said. "There are no down days."

The three girls at the bar were standing around the pool table when Al caught sight of one lad make a playful grab for the young blonde, while another lad pinched a girl's back side. He shot up out of the chair and strode over to the lad.

"Oi, hands off the girls," Al said bluntly.

"Who the fuck are you?"

"I'm the man who will decide if you leave here on your feet or on a stretcher," Al thought.

"I'm asking you nicely. Now have a drink, lads, and enjoy your day out but do not touch any of the girls," Al said with a relaxed smile.

From the corner of his eye Al could see the eight lads that Bootsie and Smudge had been talking about earlier all huddled together, talking and looking in his direction.

"This could go off," Al thought as he returned to his table.

"Fucking Northern monkeys," Smudge hissed. "No class and no respect. They should all piss off back to Geordie land."

Al looked on as three of the 'Toon Army's' top lads stood up and wandered over to the pool table. Sensing that there would be trouble, he stood up.

'TOON ARMY!

TOON ARMY!

TOON ARMY!'

All of the Newcastle United fans in the crowded pub joined in:

TOON ARMY!

TOON ARMY!

TOON ARMY!

One of the lads turned to Al, smiled and then rammed his hand up the young blonde's skirt.

Al bolted across the pub with gritted teeth and clenched fists. One lad made a grab for him. He promptly shrugged him off like a nuisance fly before landing a right hook that sent the lad off balance. The whole pub erupted into an orgy of violence. Bottles were being thrown by the locals as they steamed forward with fists and boots flying. Several of the working girls had grabbed light ale bottles and were battering anything in a black and white shirt or scarf that moved. Brian and Leaky waded forward punching, kicking and head butting anything in their way. Bootsie and Smudge rose calmly from the table, removed their jackets and rolled up their sleeves.

"Let's fucking have it!" Smudge shouted before they turned the table over and charged forward.

There were cries of pain as bones were shattered and broken. The three barmen leapt over the bar with pickaxe handles and a cosh. They waded in, swinging the pickaxe handles and battering the

Newcastle United fans to the floor, where the locals continued to kick and stomp their victims furiously.

The pub door slammed open as screaming and injured fans bolted out onto the Caledonian Road. The Bell's regulars were relentless and continued to punch, kick, batter and smash the invaders with bottles.

With the bulk of the Newcastle lads now in the streets, Al stepped back to survey the situation. Smudge had one of the top lads he'd pointed out around the throat, while he systematically punched the lad's bloody face over and over. Bootsie was kicking another of the top lads who had curled himself up into a tight ball. Black Sandra had a Light Ale beer bottle in each hand while Leaky chased a lad towards the exit and then launched an almighty kick straight up the lad's rear.

Al turned to see his brother Brian battering a giant of a man's head on the corner of the bar.

It was over… the regulars of the Bell had come together and been victorious in removing the aggressors.

Chapter 25

Al had got himself a lager, chatted with the bar staff and then joined Leaky and Brian.

"Our Newcastle United friends went on the rampage after our little tear up here," Al said as he reached into his pocket. "A few of them put a rock in a window at the jewellers and I found these."

Al put a handful of diamond rings on the table.

"Very nice Al," Leaky said as he held one up close.

"It looks like Sandy and I have found another nice little earner," Brian said as he leaned back in his chair and folded his arms triumphantly.

"Well go on then," Al said chuckling. "I know you're gagging to tell me."

"Sandy has been in to see this guy who manages part of the Kings Cross Station," Brian said.

"Yeah... and...?" Al said before taking a sip of his lager.

"Well, she laid down the foundation for me to visit," Brian said. "It looks like we're on."

"I'm not with you," Al said.

"Sandy and I have been talking about all these awayday girls travelling from the four corners of the UK to London in search of punters and making a few quid," Brian said as he unfolded his arms and leaned across the table. "Well, these girls are spending money to get here and then... they have to get home, so it looks like I'll be able to supply all their train tickets back at half price. Shit... They can even go first class if they want."

Al's ears pricked up.

"Nice one Brian, very nice," Al said as he raised his glass. "You've hit the jackpot there if all goes to plan."

"I'm seeing him again tomorrow to finalise how it'll all work, but it looks like green lights all the way," Brian said.

The door of the pub opened and in stepped three punk rockers. One of the lads wore black jeans and a ripped T-shirt with 'Pretty Vacant' written scruffily on it. His black leather jacket was covered in patches. Around his neck he wore a studded dog collar. The lad's hair had been fashioned into a four-inch centre spike and dyed bright green.

"What the fuck is one of those?" Leaky said as he watched the three punk rockers approach the bar.

"They're harmless," Al thought.

Black Sandra pulled out a chair and joined them.

"She is looking damn good," Al thought as he watched Black Sandra put her drink on the table.

"I might have a bit of business if you're interested," Black Sandra said.

"Is this me or Leaky?" Al asked with a laugh.

"I think this is more up Leaky's street," Black Sandra said with a warm smile.

"Tell me all about it," Leaky said.

Black Sandra took a deep breath, looked to her left and then her right.

"I've been seeing this girl, Amanda," Black Sandra said as she rubbed her hands. "Nice girl, married with children but has a thing for girls. Anyway, she was telling me after our last meeting that she worked at the social security offices and then out of nowhere she asked me if I was interested in ten thousand social security books for ten grand."

"That is a good price if they're the real deal," Leaky said as he reached inside his pocket and pulled out a black telephone pocketbook. "I know just the man."

"I thought you might," Black Sandra said as she slid over a sample and then turned to Al and smiled.

"Yeah, it's a fella called JB," Leaky said.

"I don't know him," Black Sandra said.

"I don't know his full name," Leaky said as he fingered through his pocketbook. "I do know that he has a thing for carving his initials into his girlfriend's arses."

"Wanker then," Black Sandra muttered.

"He has this love / hate kind of friendship with old Dickie Boyd," Leaky said as he stopped flicking through and ran his finger down the page.

"I know of Old Dickie," Black Sandra said. "He was begging down at Kings Cross until he got run over by a bus."

Leaky nodded emphatically.

"Yeah, he left here pissed as a newt and then got knocked over by a bus on his way back to his. It was a nasty business."

"Tell me about it," Black Sandra said in her broad cockney accent. "I bloody saw it! The poor sod started crossing the road and the next thing this double decker has just ploughed into him and he's gone right under the bus. I can remember standing on the pavement in absolute shock. The police arrived and started trying to help him out. Old Dickie hated the old bill more than anything on the planet and he started waving his arms about and calling them all the names under the sun as they tried to edge him out."

"Fuck me," Al thought as the images flashed through his head.

"The ambulance arrived, and still old Dickie was punching and spitting at the police. I don't think I'll ever forget seeing him finally break free and seeing he only had one leg. The blood was everywhere. The next time I saw him he was in a wheelchair," Black Sandra said.

"Well, that's where JB came in. They share the same squat, and he would help out with cooking and stuff. It's a funny relationship. I heard several times how JB would be pushing him about in his wheelchair and then after a couple of cross words he would leave Old Dickie in the middle of the road and just fuck off," Leaky said.

"Harsh," Black Sandra said.

"Did you ever meet old Dickie's rabbit, Thumper?" Leaky asked.

"I have never seen a rabbit that big in my life," Black Sandra said. "I heard that Dickie would feed the rabbit on dog food and even let it sleep in the same bed."

"It must be true," Leaky said, "because I heard the same thing.

Leaky turned to Al.

"That rabbit loved everyone, Al. All except JB," Leaky said. "The rabbit would charge at him in the squat and try to bite him at every opportunity. It hated that man with a passion."

"That rabbit was the size of a dog," Black Sandra said as she held out her arms to show the size to Al.

"Well, I heard that Old Dickie had been out begging all day and when he got home, he found JB in the kitchen cooking. By all accounts JB had laid out the table and then used a ladle to put a large helping of stew in a bowl," Leaky said. "This is what I mean about the love / hate relationship. Dickie was made up to have a hot meal waiting for him after spending a whole day begging down at Kings Cross. Seeing how quickly Dickie had been wolfing down the stew, he served him a second and then a third bowl full and then he thanked JB for cooking such a wonderful stew."

"Not such a bad guy after all then," Black Sandra said.

"Well," Leaky continued. "Once Dickie had his fill he shouted out for Thumper. He called out again and then again before turning to JB and asking where his rabbit was. Cool as you like JB announced that old Dickie had been eating him."

"Damn, I didn't see that coming," Al thought.

"And this is your friend," Black Sandra said.

"Not so much friends as business acquaintances," Leaky said as he rose from the table. "I'll give him a ring."

Five minutes later Leaky arrived back at the table carrying a tray of drinks.

"He'll be here shortly," Leaky said as he handed a drink over to Black Sandra.

"Is he good for the money?" Black Sandra said before taking a sip of her drink.

"He's a lot of things, but when it comes to business, he's first class and always pays on the nose," Leaky said.

Al took a second look at the punk rockers.

"Won't be a minute," Al said before strolling down to where the punk rockers were sat.

"Alright lads," Al said as he stopped by their table.

"Yeah, you?" the punk with the green Mohican said.

"I'm Al, Al McIntosh," Al said as he held out his hand. "I like to come and say hello to anyone who isn't a regular."

The punk shook Al's hand.

"This is my mate Riot, this is Josh and I'm Buddy."

"Nice to meet you lads," Al said as he shook Buddy's hand firmly. "So tell me, what brings you into the Bell?"

Buddy smiled and looked around the pub.

"Plenty of girls and cheap booze what else is there?"

Al smiled.

"Two great reasons to drink in here," Al said as he stepped back. "Enjoy your day lads."

Al returned to the table and found that there were two additional people sitting there.

"Al, this is JB," Leaky said as he pointed him out.

"Alright," Al said.

"This is Cleopatra," Leaky said as he pointed to an extremely short older woman in her late forties.

"Fuck me, that midget is butt ugly!" Al thought. *"Cleopatra the Egyptian beauty... is she having a laugh or what!"*

Cleopatra looked Al up and down, sneered and then turned away.

"So, Leaky you have a thousand social security books?" JB said, squinting and leaning forward.

"I have a thousand available," Leaky said as he slid the sample across the table.

JB picked it up and immediately handed it to Cleopatra.

She held it up before turning it over.

"This is genuine," Cleopatra said as she handed it to JB.

"Can you move them?"

Cleopatra smiled and then nodded.

"Piece of piss."

"What's the best price," JB said as he rubbed his finger and thumb back and forth.

"Fifteen grand and that's a steal," Leaky said before passing a sly wink to Black Sandra.

JB looked at the sample and then to Cleopatra. She nodded.

"We have a deal," JB said as he held his hand out over the table. "When can I have them?"

Black Sandra held up her five fingers and silently mouthed 'five days'.

"Five days and I'll have them all," Leaky said.

"Cash on delivery alright for you?" JB said, rising from the table.

"Sure," Leaky said as he shrugged his shoulders.

"Now that was a nice quick five thousand pounds profit," Al thought as he smiled in Black Sandra's direction.

Once JB had left the pub, Leaky handed the sample back to Black Sandra.

"What if this comes on top," Leaky said. "Is Amanda going to be alright?"

"She's sweet," Black Sandra said. "Amanda has it all sorted. On Monday the books will just be re-printed. She oversees the whole thing."

"Then it's a done deal," Leaky said. "Now, how is this going to work for you and I?"

"Half each," Black Sandra said before taking a sip of her drink.

"You are a lady, Black Sandra" Leaky said with a smile. "Let me know when you have them and we'll close the deal."

Black Sandra drank the last of her whiskey, said goodbye and left the pub.

"Brian, have you seen Wullie?"

"Not in a few weeks," Brian said, looking down at his watch.

"Me either," Al said. "Did he say anything about where he was going to or what he was up to?"

"The last thing he said to me was that Jesus had repeatedly been telling him to kill Mammy," Brian said.

"Nothing's changed there then," Al said.

Brian drank his pint and then stood up.

"I'm meeting Sandy for fish and chips," Brian said.

"And something else," Al said with a chuckle.

"Yeah, so don't wait up," Brian said as he pushed his chair under the table. "I'll see you tonight at the American Bar."

Al nodded.

"Yeah, I need to do the rounds first, but I'll be along about eleven," Al said.

Leaky motioned the barman to bring them over a couple of pints with whiskey chasers.

"Here, you remember that stripper, Shaz?" Leaky said.

"How could I forget!" Al said as he pouted his lips and expelled air.

"I did manage to track her down after that fracas here."

"Really?"

"Yeah, nice girl actually," Leaky said. "I asked her out for something to eat and a drink."

"That's not like you," Al said.

"I know, I could hardly believe the words that left my lips," Leaky said. "It was like somebody else was doing the talking and I was just the spectator."

"How did it go?" Al said.

"Remarkably well," Leaky said, rubbing his chin. "She's a real sweet girl."

"Sounds like you have a bit of a thing going on there," Al said.

"Well I like her and I don't mean because of how utterly fabulous she looked in those seamed stockings and suspenders," Leaky said, still rubbing his chin. "There was just so much more to the person that took her clothes off."

"Well I'm pleased for you mate," Al said.

"Yeah, she told me that lived in some godforsaken town in Scotland and had married this lunatic she'd known since school. He would come home drunk and start arguments and then," Leaky said screwing up his face, "the bastard would batter her black and blue."

"I can't bear to hear about men hitting woman," Al said.

"Me either," Leaky said. "It makes me want to start pulling heads off."

"So she got out, then?" Al said.

"Yeah, her mother gave Shaz the train fare and a few quid to see her through and the rest is history," Leaky said. "She's been London almost a year now."

"It's funny because when I saw her up there strutting about looking like sex on legs, I just wanted to fuck her brains out but now that we know each other, I just want to chat and enjoy her company. Don't get me wrong, I still fancy the pants off her but it's not a top priority now," Leaky said.

"Do you have anyone special?" Leaky said softly.

Al shook his head.

"With so many available girls I'm just not looking for anything serious," Al said as he turned to his friend. "Besides I have so much yet that I still want to achieve."

"Al," the barman called out as he held up the telephone.

Al was up and over to the bar in seconds.

Al: Hello.

Caller: Its Black Sandra, Al. A car has just pulled up outside the squat and it's those debt collectors again.

Al: What's your address? I'm on my way.

Al scribbled down the address and hung up.

"I've got a situation to take care of," Al said as he passed Leaky. "I'll catch you later."

Leaky shot up with such speed it knocked his chair over.

"Hold up, I'll come with you," Leaky said as he clambered out from behind the table.

On the way to the Kings Cross address Al filled in the background to Black Sandra's situation.

"Bully boys getting off on intimidating women then," Leaky said.

Al nodded.

Al pushed the front door open and bounded up the short flight of stairs to the first floor. The door was open. Al stepped into the front room to find two debt collectors knocking ornaments off the shelf.

"Who the fuck are you?" the red headed debt collector said as he pounded his fist into his hand.

"Well, I'm not a pregnant girl," Al said racing forward.

The redheaded debt collector threw a clumsy punch that shot past Al's head. Al fired a short sharp punch that connected with his target's chin. The debt collector threw a second punch which left his body wide open. Al raised his fists and fired a succession of left and right hooks before releasing an almighty uppercut.

Leaky clenched both fists and charged forward to the second debt collector. Before his target had a chance to respond, Leaky let loose a powerful bomb of a punch that threw his victim off balance. He staggered back onto the balcony, and before he could recover Leaky smashed his fist into his head with such ferocity that the debt collector fell back against the wrought iron fence on the balcony. A second head shot, and the debt collector went clean over the top. Leaky watched as the debt collector fell from the first floor and landed on the roof of a green Morris Marina.

With adrenaline racing through his veins, Al pounded out one brutal punch after another. He paused for a millisecond, took aim, and threw several more heavy punches. The debt collector rolled his eyes before collapsing and falling awkwardly to the floor.

Al bent down and grabbed him by the scruff of his collar before dragging him along the carpet and into the hallway. Without stopping Al dragged him out of the first floor flat and then rolled him out over the stairs. With a single kick from his right foot the debt collector was sent sprawling head over heels down the stairs.

Al turned to see Black Sandra and her two flatmates looking at him.

Chapter 26

Shortly after the debt collector incident, Al found that increasingly Black Sandra would be around where he was. He would look up from his table and Black Sandra would be moving her body in rhythm to the song on the jukebox. Al would see her at the bar, and she would pass a short sideways darting glance that lasted a couple of seconds. Black Sandra would join them at the table and during a story she would flip her head backwards and lift her face briefly. Al felt that she was showing interest but couldn't be sure, and he didn't want to spoil a friendship by making a clumsy pass. On more than one occasion when Al handed her a drink, she would move her torso and upper body forward so she got closer to him.

Leaky was up at the bar when Black Sandra suddenly turned sharply towards Al.

"Al," Black Sandra said with a tooth revealing smile.

"Yes," Al said.

"I no longer want to be just friends with you," Black Sandra said with a sultry, seductive smile.

Al beamed.

"You do know what I mean by that... don't you?"

"I think so," Al said.

"I want a relationship where you and I spend time together without any conditions or boundaries," Black Sandra said, while holding her intense gaze.

Al felt his mouth go dry and nodded.

"There will be no romance, no love, no expectations and no commitment to each other. We will have fun, laugh and be the best of friends but there can be no bond holding us together," Black Sandra said, still holding Al's gaze.

"You've given this some thought," Al said as he allowed a smile to slowly spread across his face.

"Will that work for you Al McIntosh?"

"So, if I like a girl...?" Al said cautiously.

"Like I said, we will have no expectations or boundaries," Black Sandra said as she softened her gaze. "I will not justify to you or anyone else what decisions I make with my body."

Leaky put a tray of drinks on the table.

Al handed Black Sandra a tumbler of whiskey and then took one himself.

"To friendship," Al said as he raised his glass towards Black Sandra.

"A special friendship," Black Sandra said before taking a long sip from her glass.

Al turned to the bar to see Brian surrounded by working girls. He was handing something out and taking money back.

"What's he up to?" Al wondered.

Brian returned to the table carrying a fistful of notes.

"I told you, didn't I?" Brian said and put the notes into his pocket.

"Told me what?" Al said.

"There was money in this whole awayday thing," Brian said.

"You mean, Kings Cross Station?" Al said.

Brian nodded and then patted his pocket.

"I've pulled in just over three thousand pounds this week from awayday train tickets," Brian gloated. "Everyone is a winner."

"I'm pleased for you," Al said.

"Life is so sweet I can bloody well taste it," Al thought as he glanced around the table. *"Everyone is making good money and I have a no strings thing with Black Sandra. What more could a bloke want?"*

"How is business for you?" Al said as he turned towards Leaky.

"Couldn't be better," Leaky said. "Bootsie and Smudge are taking the cheque books, the girls are buying caseloads of fivers from me daily, and my latest little venture, Giros, with a combined value of one thousand pounds sold out at four hundred quid in minutes. At this rate I'll be working longer than I am in the pub!"

"You have to take it while it's there," Al said.

"What's all this I've heard about private sex shows in the Bell?" Brian said as he wiped the lager froth from his mouth.

"I heard that too," Leaky said.

"It's true," Black Sandra said. "I told you sex always sells. Jenny Ling has half a dozen pretty girls and has been doing sex shows like me, only my girls do the whole lesbian thing before pulling up paying punters. Jenny has a sweet little number. All her girls either have boyfriends or are married. Keep this to yourselves, but Jenny puts on these shows and charges fifty quid a head. They sell out... They always sell out. After stripping off the girls will play with each other and then pull up guys from the audience and put on a show by sucking them off. What the paying punters don't know is that the guys being publicly relieved are, in fact, their husbands or boyfriends. Very clever girl, is Jenny, you have to take your hat off to her."

"What if some bloke pulls down his trousers?" Leaky said.

"Then the girls will hold up their hand firmly and remain focused on the boyfriend or husband," Black Sandra said.

"Well, remind me not to go," Leaky said.

"Yeah, me too," Brian said.

"I might still go," Al thought.

"Excuse me, Al."

Al looked up to see Buddy the punk and his two mates.

"You seem to be the man to talk to around here," Buddy said.

"How can I help you?" Al asked.

"We'd like to organise a gig, you know bring in a punk band," Buddy said. "It'll bring people into the pub, so drinks sales should be good."

"As long as everyone has a good time and behaves themselves, I've got no problem with you lads organising a band for the pub."

"Nice one," Buddy said before turning back and smiling at his two mates.

Chapter 27

"How are you getting on with Shaz?" Al asked as he slid a glass of whiskey across the table to Leaky.

"Yeah, alright I suppose," Leaky said.

"That doesn't sound too good."

"We've been out a few times and I really do enjoy chatting and hanging out with her, but the other night she just looked and smelt so damn good, I made a bit of a move and she turned on me. I mean this was not the Shaz that I had spent hours chatting to. I pushed her a little as to why and she started going on about wanting respect and not wanting to rush anything. Look Al, I get all that, but it wears a bit thin when you know that directly after leaving me, she will take money for sex with a complete stranger," Leaky said as he raised his glass.

"Maybe you're giving it too much thought," Al said.

"You could be right, Al. Before I started seeing Shaz, I was happy... actually very happy just meeting with a couple of regular girls. We would play games with toys and when it's all over we go our separate ways until the next time."

"I think you'd frighten the life out of Shaz if you turned up with that Empire State building of a dildo," Al thought with a slight chuckle.

"I heard today that Dougie 'The Man' McKinnon got weighed off for four years," Leaky said before turning to watch a young brunette in a short red tartan skirt and stiletto heels pass the table.

"I don't like to hear about anyone getting sent down," Al said as he followed Leaky's gaze. "But after what he did to SAS... fuck him."

"Four years.... He'll probably be out in two," Al thought.

Al had a sip of his drink and took a quick look around the pub. There seemed to be groups of working girls all chatting and getting agitated.

"Have you seen anything of SAS?" Al said, watching one of the girls becoming very animated as she spoke.

"I did see him just after he got out of hospital," Leaky said. "He's done with this place. To be honest, I think he's too scared to even go out after the beating Dougie gave him."

Black Sandra waved from the far end of the bar and then strolled over to join them.

"I'm just going to get a round in," Leaky said as he rose from the table.

Sandra slid in alongside Al. She opened her handbag and nudged him to look inside.

"I've got my gun," Black Sandra whispered.

Al turned and looked down at the matt black Beretta handgun.

"You'll need to careful with that," Al said.

"I'm going to find the bastard that raped me and kill him," Black Sandra hissed. "I went out last night looking around the Kings Cross area for him. I will find him, and he will die at my hands."

"Carrying a gun is automatic time behind bars," Al whispered. "Just be careful."

Leaky returned to the table with blonde Lucy with the pig tails and two of her friends, Lotte and Kate.

"It all seems to be going on out there on the streets," Leaky said as he sat down.

"There's just no respect for the hierarchy," Kate said in her broad Stoke accent as she slapped the palm of her hand down on the table.

Kate had a willowy figure that accentuated her curves. Her ringlets of bleached blonde hair wreathed her moon shaped face.

"Those girls were just bullying their way into our action," Lotte said.

"Are you hearing this?" Leaky said.

"What exactly is the problem?" Al said as he squeezed Black Sandra's leg.

"From out of nowhere there are scores of black girls just pitching up in our regular spots," Lucy said with a short sharp sigh.

"These girls have pimps too," said Lotte. "I've seen them. Carloads of mean looking guys with dreadlocks."

"What do you know about them?" Al said.

"Leicester," Kate said. "I was told that a whole crew of guys and girls came down from Leicester. It's like they want to take over our bit of action."

"Well, I'm not giving up my patch," Lucy said indignantly. "I came to London because we were piss poor with red warning notices arriving daily through the letterbox. Kings Cross has been good to me. I'm making proper money that keeps the debtors at bay, food on the table and clothes on my daughter's back. I'm telling you now... I will not be intimidated by a carload of pimps!"

"I'm having the time of my life," Kate said as she reached for her drink. "This beats sitting indoors watching Coronation Street and then a Saturday Night out at the working man's club. Down here in London I have my own place, good clothes, money in my pocket and I'm having a damn good time with people who are living for the moment. Like you, Lucy, I will not be moved."

"Maybe you girls should consider working in a brothel," Black Sandra said. "The clients come to you, and if a punter gets a little handy then security is either on site or just a few minutes away. It's safer."

"It did cross my mind," Lucy said as she turned to Black Sandra. "I was talking with a couple of girls from Madge's brothel in Finsbury Park. Nice girls. I met them at your American Bar, Al."

"That's not the point though, is it?" Kate said firmly. "You can't just roll over because someone wants to take what you've worked for."

"This is beginning to sound like a lot more than just a few new girls trying it on," Al thought. *"If they have men behind them and they've come all the way down from Leicester then these lads have other, more hostile, things on their mind. This place, if you know what you're doing, is a goldmine, so we'll all need to stay on our toes."*

"What we girls do is no walk in the park," Black Sandra said in a forceful, decisive, tone. "I've been robbed three times, beaten up twice and raped once in the last two years. These bastards know that we can't to go to the police and so to some of these punters we can be seen as prey. I had one guy proposition me and when I got into his car, he produced a warrant card…. Yeah, you got it he was old bill. I thought I'd be nicked for prostitution but oh no, he had other things on his mind. He wanted oral and he wanted it for free. So I'm faced with being taken to the police station, held in a cell and then get whatever the judge decides is right for me that day or I do what I have to do. This sly bastard liked it so much that he wanted more, and he didn't want to pay for it, so he kept the threat of arrest over me."

"The bastard!" Kate said.

"I made him pay though," Black Sandra said with a wry smile. "I had one of my friends take a Polaroid of me performing oral in his car. She snapped the picture and bolted off up the road. He had no chance what with his trousers around his knees. It was a damn good picture, showing his stupid face and me with my head in his lap. I had him... I had that bastard's balls in the palm of my hand, and I was ready to squeeze."

"He must have been shitting himself," Lucy said.

Black Sandra nodded.

"He couldn't get his trousers up fast enough," Black Sandra said as she balled her fist. "I found out what station he was at and then had an envelope left for him at the main desk with his name on it. It had a copy of the picture and a note that simply said one thousand pounds, or your wife, family and superior officers will all get their own personal copy."

Lucy and Kate began to laugh.

"Good for you," Lotte said. "Did he pay up?"

"It wasn't about the money," Black Sandra said. "He was trying to control me through fear. I waited and then sent the pictures out. I thought fuck him. He was a bully in a uniform, and he needed to go."

"Did you ever see him again?" Lotte said as she leaned across the table and rested her chin on her hands.

"He must have resigned or been booted out because I did see him in Tooting a year or so later. I was with my girls on the way to a private show when I spotted him walking along carrying a satchel and dressed in a postman's uniform."

"I like that," Kate said.

"Me too," Lotte said.

"What would you do if you were us?" Lucy said.

Black Sandra reached down into her handbag for the Beretta handgun. She raised it slowly so that everyone at the table could see it before putting it down next to her drink.

"If a person wants to take what is mine, threaten or attempt to hurt me, I'll blow their fucking heads off!" Black Sandra said with her eyes fixed on Lucy.

"Fucking hell, the last thing we want are working girls running around Kings Cross tooled up with shooters," Al thought as he watched Black Sandra put the gun back into her handbag. *"The old bill will be down here in big numbers, sticking their noses in where it's not wanted and that simply isn't good for business."*

"Don't you girls be rushing out to buy shooters," Al said calmly. "Later tonight my brother Brian, Leaky and I will take a wander out on the streets and have a quiet word with these girls and their pimps, okay?"

"You would do that?" Kate said with a look of surprise.

"Yes, of course," Al said with a smile. "What we all have here is working well and we can't have that spoilt."

"Did you hear what happened to Laurel and Hardy?" Kate asked.

Laurel and Hardy were two working girls that arrived in London from Middlesbrough. They had a niche market in the city. The girls would both dress up as the movie comic stars Laurel and Hardy, and then perform an explicit lesbian show and charge one thousand pounds. It had become extremely popular with their shows booked months in advance.

"No," Lucy said as she shook her head.

"Well, I heard that they were planning to rob a bank and Laurel went out and bought herself a gun. It was at an after-show party that they both did several lines of cocaine."

"Not always a good thing," Lucy said. "It can make you do silly things that you regret later."

"Yeah, they were both well and truly out of their heads," Kate said. "I don't know who suggested it, but the pair of them went off down to a bank in Finsbury, both still dressed up as Laurel and Hardy, and they've marched into the bank and demanded the money. The alarms went off and they scurried off out with just three hundred pounds. They didn't even get to the end of the road before the old bill had swooped in."

"Just three hundred quid," Lucy said in disbelief. "I would have thought that robbing a bank was big money.... you know thousands... hundreds of thousands."

"It shocked me," Kate said as she slowly shook her head. "Although I couldn't help smiling to myself when I imagined them trying to hold up a bank all dressed up as Laurel and Hardy."

"There's a lesson to be learned here," Al said as he moved his serious gaze from one girl to the next. "That silly escapade will cost them five years if they're lucky. Now if they kept their heads down and continued with their private 'fetish' sex shows at a thousand pounds per show at one per week then that three-hundred-pound robbery has lost them two hundred and fifty thousand pounds tax free income."

"Fuck me," Kate said with a sigh. "I never thought about it like that. I mean...two hundred and fifty thousand pounds. That is life changing money."

***

After another couple of drinks and with 'I'm Every Woman' by Chaka Khan playing in the background, Black Sandra and the girls left the Bell.

"What do you make of this Leicester thing?" Leaky said as he poured Al a whiskey.

"Between you and me, Leaky, I've got a bad feeling about this," Al said softly. "Don't get me wrong, I don't give a fuck who they are, but this just doesn't feel like a coincidence."

"I agree," Leaky said. "If just half of what's being said is true, this firm has turned up mob handed."

"We need to know more about who and what we may have to deal with," Al said.

"I have a few friends in Leicester," Leaky said before downing a full glass of whiskey. "I can make a few phone calls."

"Yeah, I like that," Al said, rubbing his hands together.

"I'll do it now," Leaky said, and then walked over to the bar to use the pub's phone.

Brian brought a tray of drinks over to the table as *'Shooting Star'* by Dollar played.

"It has been one brilliant week," Brian said as he puffed out his chest. "Sandy has got us a key to Kings Cross Station so now we can just help ourselves to more registered letters. Today we pulled in just over four thousand pounds and with the awayday tickets, this week has earned us nearly nine thousand pounds."

"Very nice," Al said.

"Are you alright?" Brian said as he turned to his brother.

"Yeah, it's probably nothing," Al said, patting Brian on the shoulder. "Well done, Brian."

Leaky returned to the table.

"Did you speak to your contacts?" Al said as he leaned across the table.

Leaky nodded.

"There's a fired up mob from St Matthews in Leicester with brothers, sisters, cousins and friends in Highfields, Beaumont Leys and the Saffron Estate," Leaky said softly. "They run the girls on street corners, brothels, drugs, extortion and control the doors on the nightclubs. They've been credited with beatings, stabbings and two murders. There are no rules with these animals. It's anything goes. My contact said that even the old bill give them a swerve which tells me they have people on the payroll."

"They're fucking organised," Al thought. *"My gut feeling was right."*

"What's all this then?" Brian said.

Al and Leaky brought Brian up to date about new girls from Leicester taking over spots on the street corners and car loads of men patrolling the streets.

"We can't be having this!" Brian said, shaking his emphatically. "We've both come a long way since those Balgrayhill Boys. This needs to be stamped down on!"

"We need to keep this under wraps," Al said. "I told Lucy and her friends that the three of us will take a walk around Kings Cross and have a quiet word with any Leicester girls and their pimps."

"Fucking right," Brian said. "If one of them even looks at me the wrong way I'll bite his fucking face."

"Are you alright with this, Leaky?" Al asked as he stood up.

"I live for shit like this," Leaky said as he clenched both fists and smiled.

The three men walked around the main roads and side streets of Kings Cross. They smiled and acknowledged the working girls they knew. Kerb crawlers filled the street with punters looking for sex.

"I have the utmost respect for these girls," Al said.

"Me too," Leaky said as he waved to a girl he knew. "I do think that sixteen is a little too young to be on the streets, though. Maybe eighteen would be better."

"How would you know their age?" Brian asked bluntly. "It's dark and with their make-up, short skirts and heels you just wouldn't know."

"Maybe..." Leaky said.

"Well, see that girl over there?" Brian said as he pointed to a young girl in a short white dress, white socks and trainers standing beside a lamppost. "How old would you say she was?"

"Eighteen... maybe twenty," Leaky said.

"I would say mid to late twenties but made up to look younger," Al said.

"You see now, you are eight to ten years apart," Brian said. "How would you know sixteen, eighteen or even twenty-five?"

"Visually I agree with you Brian, but I was thinking that a slightly older girl would be more confident and capable of making decisions about this kind of work," Leaky said.

"You make it sound like a career choice, like it was for you when you turned your back on a hundred-thousand-pound home and a hundred thousand pounds in the bank. No one truly knows what happened to these girls or what lead them to working the streets of London," Al thought as he strode down Caledonian Road.

"The girls I speak to say it's just a job and sex is just work and that everyone has to make a living the best way they can," Leaky said. "I met one girl, Rachel, pretty little thing, and she told me that she loved having sex with different, interesting, men and women. She saw it as a kind of hobby that paid well."

"I'm sure that she's just one in a hundred... maybe even a thousand," Al said.

"I've probably spoken and listened to more prostitutes than both of you." Al thought as he scanned the streets. *"Most of these girls didn't make a conscious choice to go on the game, strip or do sex*

shows. It was a path that opened for them because of their need to make money and support their partners, children and in some cases the entire family. Many of the girls I've listened to have shaken off the stigma and become confident and even powerful because they are able to do this. Yeah, I admire and respect these girls. Living a double life cannot be easy."

"Not a single Leicester girl on the street, no problem so it's back for a pint then," Leaky said.

Al stopped and took one last look up and down Caledonian Road.

"Maybe they fucked off back to Leicester," Brian muttered.

'Crazy Little Thing Called Love' by Queen was playing on the jukebox as Al stepped back into the Bell.

Al and Brian sat at their usual table while Leaky went to the bar.

"Brian, I'm away this weekend to Bristol. Can you get me a ticket?"

Brian looked up at the girl and smiled.

"No problem I'll have it tomorrow night.

"My friend Candy wants a return ticket to Sunderland too," the pretty brunette said.

Brian took out his notebook, flicked through the outstanding orders before writing in Bristol and Sunderland.

"This is a licence to print money," Brian said as he turned to Al.

"The whole of Kings Cross is, and we'll need to be ready to defend it by any and all means necessary," Al thought.

'Take That to the Bank' by Shalamar was playing when Leaky returned to the table with the tray of drinks.

Just as Al was about to take a sip of his ice-cold lager, the pub's door slammed open, and Lucy raced in and over to his table.

"It's Kate!" Lucy said as she bent forward to catch her breath.

"What's happened," Al said as he shot up.

"It was one of those Leicester girls," Lucy said before taking a deep breath and standing up straight. "This girl has just swaggered over to Kate's spot and Kate, being Kate, has told the bitch to fuck the hell off. When the girl started giving her lip, Kate has smacked the bitch straight in the face. There was blood everywhere and the bitch fucked off."

"Yeah... and?" Al said.

"This car has screeched to halt, and these four big black lads jumped out. They grabbed Kate and bundled her into the car. I ran over to the car and began to pound on the roof while screaming to let her go. Those fucking animals were laughing as they tore off her clothes. Then this one guy looked up at me through the window and held up a pair of pliers. Al, he was fucking evil. He grabbed Kate by the throat, showed her the pliers and then ripped off her nipple!"

"What?" Leaky said in disbelief.

"They bundled her out of the car onto the road and just roared off," Lucy said as tears streamed down her face. "I tried to help her, I really did, but there was nothing I could do."

Al could see a growing crowd listening to Lucy's story.

"I've been hearing about these Leicester mugs," Baldy hissed.

"Scum, low life fucking scum," Tony Mays growled.

"Where is Kate now?" Al asked.

"I called the ambulance and waited with Kate until it arrived and then raced back here to avoid getting questioned by the old bill," Lucy said.

"You did all you could," Al said calmly. "There are many that would have turned and run but you didn't."

"I'm afraid," Lucy said as she wiped her tears away with her sleeve. "That could have been me or any of the regular girls. The Leicester lot are truly evil bastards."

"They've sent a message," Al thought as he looked around at the growing sea of angry, confused and frightened faces. *"There will be more, and it won't be one all out fight because of the police, witnesses and Kings Cross is too big an area. But more importantly, it won't be good for business"*

Chapter 28

"I wonder if she'll still be seeing special clients," Leaky said as he poured Al a large whiskey.

"Who?" Al said as he took a small sip.

"Blow Job," Leaky said. "I like Blow Job, she's a nice girl."

"Yeah, I heard she can do special things with her tongue," Al thought to himself with a wry smile.

"I have to say that I didn't see that coming," Leaky said as he slowly shook his head.

"Why?" said Al.

"I suppose you have to ask yourself if you can really feel love, compassion and devotion to a woman who sleeps with men for a living?" Leaky said before drinking his full glass of whiskey. "These girls, all the girls around here, are about giving men a fantasy and making money for themselves. It a commercial transaction and it works. And works well."

"It wasn't that long ago Leaky, that you were telling me you had developed feelings for Shaz," Al thought.

"I know what you're thinking," Leaky said as he refilled his glass. "I decided that Shaz and I would be just good friends and I would continue to see my regular set of girls."

"Maybe I just see things a little different from you," Al said as he put his glass back on the table and leaned forward. "I believe that a man can still fall in love with a working girl because despite what she does to get by and pay the bills, she is still a woman, and she still has virtues."

Leaky listened intently.

"I'm sure that Blow Job has her flaws, as does Tony," Al said. "Let's face it mate… we all do. I think Tony is a good guy and if he can make a good go of sharing a life with Blow Job then good on them both."

Tony Mays and Blow Job had announced their plans to marry a few days before. They decided that Tony would continue to provide security for Madge's brothel in Gloucester Drive and Blow Job would now only see female clients. Everyone at the Bell pub was pleased for them and suggested a celebration drink.

The pub door swung open, and Tony entered the pub dressed in a blue suit with a white, open neck shirt.

"Hurrah!" the locals and punters in search of girls yelled as he approached the bar.

The barman put a full glass of whiskey in front of Tony and then pointed over to Al's table. Tony picked up the glass, turned to Al and raised his glass.

Al and Leaky both raised theirs to him and mouthed 'cheers' to the sound of *'Woman in Love'* by The Three Degrees.

Al watched as Baldy, blonde Lucy with the pig tails, Lotte and others from around the pub shook Tony's hand or patted him warmly on the shoulder.

Tony held up his drink and called out 'cheers'.

"DRINK…DRINK…DRINK!"

The Bell's locals all roared.

"Down in one!" Baldy yelled as he raised his glass.

Tony took a deep breath, smiled and put the glass to his lips.

"Woohoo!" Lucy and Lotte bellowed as one.

"DRINK...DRINK...DRINK!" the locals continued.

Tony tipped his glass back and gulped down the contents. He held up the empty glass.

His achievement was met with an eruption of cheers and the raucous clapping of hands.

Tony put the empty glass on the bar, turned back to his friends and raised both hands in the air.

"I'm getting married!" Tony cried, while the barman replaced his drink.

Baldy stood up and motioned the cheering regulars to calm down. Once the cheers stopped, he cleared his throat and smiled.

"Tony... all your friends at the Bell have clubbed together to bring you..." Baldy said as he pointed to the barman.

The beginning of the wedding march tune began to pound out of the speakers.

"We give you... the very sexy...Shaz!"

The ladies' toilet door swung open and there stood Shaz dressed in a stunning Tulle V-neck full length white wedding dress complete with a matching veil. Her hair had been fashioned into a centre parting and brought together into a single pig tail, accompanied by long sparkly earrings. As the wedding march played, she took slow pigeon steps out into the middle of the bar with her hands clasped together. Shaz stopped and faced Tony.

The music came to an abrupt halt as *'I'm Gonna Love You Just A Little More Baby'* by Barry White belted out from the speaker system. Shaz moved her right arm around to her waist and tore the wedding dress clean off in one single movement. Everyone in the pub stood up and cheered as it revealed a very short white lace cocktail dress with an illusion neckline, lace cap sleeves and a fitted bodice with lace appliques. The waist was wrapped by an embellished belt and the thigh high A–Line skirt curled at the hem.

Shaz began to swing her hips suggestively back and forth in time to the heavy drumbeat.

Lads from around the bar began to wolf whistle as the little lace skirt rose up, revealing her white fish net stocking tops and suspenders.

Shaz danced back and forth while thrusting and gyrating her hips in an evocative figure of eight movement.

"Get them off!" one lad cried out as he clambered onto a table to gain a better view.

Shaz strutted up and down the bar in her super high white stiletto heels as 'Do You Wanna Touch Me' by Joan Jett & The Blackhearts pounded out of the speakers.

Together everyone in the pub sang out 'Yeah... Oh Yeah... Oh Yeah," just before Shaz stopped once again, scanned the room slowly and then ripped off the cocktail dress in one rapid movement and threw it at Tony. Shaz continued to circle her hips provocatively in her white fish net stockings, suspenders and matching silk panties before reaching around and releasing her white lace bra.

As she swung her delicate, iridescent pert breasts, almost everyone in the pub cheered rowdily at the top of their voices.

Shaz took sedate, sexy steps towards Tony in her white stiletto heels, leaned forward and kissed him gently on the head. The song came to a sudden ending with Shaz turning swiftly on her heels, collecting up her discarded clothing and bolting back towards the ladies' toilet.

Tony, his friends and everyone in the bar clapped enthusiastically.

"I don't think Tony will forget that in a hurry," Al said as he watched Tony read the menu and put a coin in the jukebox.

'I Only Want to Be With You' by the Tourists began to play.

The pub door opened and in stepped eight black men. The one leading the pack wore blue jeans, a tight white vest that showed off his muscular physique and a heavy gold necklace. His hair, like all the others, was fashioned like rope strands braided into long dreadlocks. A second man scanned the room as he entered. He wore a beige and brown chequered suit and a chocolate-coloured shirt with a butterfly collar.

"Fuck me, the circus is in town," Leaky whispered.

Al watched intently as all eight men paraded through the pub before stopping at the bar.

"This little lot are no mugs," Al thought as he kept his eyes fixed on the group. *"They come from the same impoverished background as me."*

"Do you reckon Huggy Bear will give an autograph?" Leaky said as he nodded towards the Leicester lad in the chequered suit.

Huggy Bear was a character from the popular Starsky and Hutch television series.

"This is no coincidence," Al thought. *"Step one of their plan was to send a message of violence and now, by turning up mob handed, they mean to intimidate us."*

Al watched as the pub quietened down. Small gatherings whispered and looked on as the Leicester Lads drank and laughed loudly at the bar. Baldy stepped away from a group and strutted confidently over to the fearsome mob at bar.

"This is a showdown," Al thought as Baldy stopped in front of the muscular Leicester lad in the tight white vest.

The Leicester lad turned to face Baldy and gave him a menacing stare. One by one the other lads swivelled round.

Baldy was not intimidated by the lad's size or physique.

"Which one of you ripped Kate's nipple?" Baldy said, his eyes fixed on the lads.

The merry, joyful atmosphere had sizzled away to one of dread and anticipation of impending brutal violence.

"Fucking sewer rats!" Leaky hissed as he swallowed the last of his drink.

'Too Much Heaven' by the Bee Gees was on the jukebox.

The Leicester lad looked Baldy up and down before revealing a crazed smile.

"I did it... now fuck off, you bald bastard!"

The other lads began to jeer Baldy as he turned and walked back to his chair.

"London is a jungle full of vicious, violent people hungry to get ahead and some of the most ruthless are here in Kings Cross," Al thought as he watched Baldy calmly reach into his black sports bag and pull out a heavy motorcycle chain.

Baldy wrapped the end of the chain around his fist, took a deep breath, and then, unperturbed, sauntered back to the bar. He stood just a few feet away from the lad in the white vest. Baldy raised his arm allowing the weighty metal motorcycle chain to fall behind him. As the lad in the chequered suit turned, Baldy let out a loud roar and swung the chain with all his might.

"Arghh," the lad shrieked as the chain slammed into and then ripped through the flesh on his face.

The lad fell to his knees with both hands cupping his face. The blood gushed through his fingers onto the threadbare carpet.

"Arghh!" he cried out again as Baldy swung the chain a second time with such ferocity that it slashed and tore open big chunks of skin on his arm and chest.

Al and Leaky were both up and charging towards the bar with gritted teeth and clenched fists. Tony steamed forward and threw a powerful right hook that sent another lad to the floor. Several men raced forward and began to kick the floored aggressor. With one hand on the bar, Tony yelled and repeatedly stomped on the lad's head.

Al narrowly missed a knife jab. The lad had over stretched himself and left his side open. Al instinctively swivelled around, found the angle and unleashed a series of savage hooks, kicks and then a hefty uppercut that buckled the lad's legs. He dropped the blade and swayed like a drunk on a bender. Al bulldozed him with several lethal, brain scrambling, headshots. The lad's legs collapsed, and he fell to the floor like a rag doll.

Lucy grabbed a Light Ale bottle from the bar and smashed it over the back of another lad's head after Leaky pile-drove his mighty fist into his victim's face. With blood streaming out of the back of his head, Lucy dropped the bottle and grabbed another. Refusing to go down, the lad threw one punch after another. One caught Leaky off guard. It landed on his chin sending a shock wave through his body. Sensing that Leaky was on the back foot he threw a second and then a third punch. Al grabbed a wrought iron bar stool by the base and with herculean force swung it, smashing into his target's face, shattering teeth and splintering bones. As the lad fell backwards, Lucy brought the second beer bottle crashing down on his head. As he lay on the floor, Lucy, filled with hate from what had happened to her friend Kate, cried out 'You fucking bastards!" while stomping on the lad's leg and thigh in her heels.

With a firm grip on the wrought iron bar stool, Al turned briskly, ready to release brutal violence on another adversary. All eight Leicester lads had been battered, kicked, punched, bottled and viciously beaten.

Leaky was the first to grab a lad by the collar of his black leather box jacket and pull his limp body across the pub carpet over to the door. Lotte held it open as Leaky pulled the semi-conscious Leicester lad out onto the pavement and dumped his broken and beaten body by the rubbish bins. Tony grabbed another, followed by Al and a few of the other men. Within a few minutes all eight Leicester lads lay out on the roadside. On Al's instruction, the barman called the ambulance as an anonymous member of the public.

Al reached into his pocket and pulled out a large wad of notes. He held them up for everyone to see.

"Drinks all round on me!" Al said as he put the notes onto the bar.

"Tony, are you alright?" Al said as he pointed to a large patch of blood on his white shirt.

"It's just a nick, Al," Tony said before taking a long sip from his fresh pint. "The silly bastard tried to stab me.

Tony reached into his pocket and pulled out a switchblade.

"I stamped on the mugs hand," Tony said as he pressed the button and allowed the blade to fire out from the top of the shaft. "He isn't going to be stabbing anyone with that hand for a while."

"The ambulances are outside," Lucy said as she reached for a drink. "I need this!"

"That slag caught me unawares," Leaky said as he chinked glasses with Al. "I appreciate that."

"It can happen to anyone... anytime," Al said as the pub door opened, and two uniformed police officers stepped inside.

"It's the old bill," muttered Al as he swiftly turned to Tony. "Do your jacket up."

As the officers moved across the pub, Al spotted the three stripes on the senior officer's shoulder.

"He's a Sergeant," Al thought before turning his back on them.

"Right, I'd like your attention please," the Police Sergeant said.

'The Eton Rifles' by The Jam was booming out of the jukebox.

"Turn that racket off!" the Police Sergeant said to the barman, pointing at the jukebox.

The barman looked at Al before moving.

Al nodded.

The barman walked out from behind the bar, over to the jukebox and then reached down and pulled the plug out.

"So, it's you I need to be talking to then," the Police Sergeant said as he stopped in front of Al.

Al shrugged his shoulders.

"I am Sergeant Faulkner, and this is my patch," he said while addressing everyone in the pub. "That steaming pile of shit out on the pavement is responsible for an attack on a young girl, intimidating local businesses and for several unprovoked stabbings. As far as I'm concerned, they're nothing more than feral scum that need locking away."

Silence reigned across the Bell pub.

Sergeant Faulkner turned back to Al.

"If you have any sway here, do us all a favour and have some of your people come forward as witnesses, and I'll ensure they are locked away for a long, long time," Sergeant Faulkner said in a lowered tone.

Al took a deep breath before raising his head to meet the Police Sergeant's intent stare head on.

"I'm sorry... we can't help you." Al said firmly.

Chapter 29

Al, Brian, Leaky, Black Sandra and JB were drinking at the Bell.

"Cleopatra has cashed in all those social security books. It went sweet as a nut," JB said with a broad grin. "Do you have any more?"

From the corner of his eye Leaky caught Black Sandra nodding gently.

"Yeah, no problem," Leaky said. "Same as before, ten thousand books for fifteen grand?"

"Deal," JB said as he reached across the table to shake Leaky's hand. "Do you have anything else?"

"Not at the minute, but as you know that can change at any time," Leaky said.

"Give me a call when you have the books," JB said as he stood up from the table.

Everyone at the table looked over as the pub door opened and a six-foot-tall skinny lad with a bright red Mohawk hairstyle stepped in. He wore a black biker style leather jacket covered in clashing political symbol badges. Around his neck he had a black leather dog collar with large silver pointed studs. His faded blue jeans were aesthetically ripped and held together with king size safety pins.

"What the...?" Leaky whispered.

"Fuck me," JB said as his jaw dropped open.

"It's Johnny Rotten," Sandy said as she stared at the punk rocker.

"Johnny Rotten doesn't have green hair," Brian said as he casually reached for his pint.

"Alright," the punk said as he approached their table. "I'm looking for Al."

Al stood up and looked the punk rocker up and down.

"Who wants to know?" Al said curtly.

"GBH."

"You what?" Al said.

"I'm GBH, lead singer of Teenage Kleptos. We're playing here later."

Al smiled.

"Yeah, that's right. I remember now. You're mates with Buddy, right?" Al said as he sat back in his seat.

"Alright to bring the gear in?" GBH said as he scanned the pub.

"Yeah, you can set yourselves up over there," Al said as he pointed to the far end of the pub.

GBH nodded and headed back out of the door.

"How can they walk around looking like that?" Leaky said.

"They're just youngsters protesting through music, culture and dress," Al said. "It's just a bit of provocative fun and finger pointing at the establishment."

"Those punk girls are sexy as fuck," Al thought as the image of the girls he'd seen in Lewisham back in 1977 flashed through his mind.

"The whole punk rock thing has been spreading like a virus into the suburbs since the Sex Pistols appeared with Bill Grundy on the Today programme," JB said.

"I watched that," Sandy said. "I thought my old mum was going to faint when they started swearing. Dad spilt his boiling hot tea over his lap. To be honest I found the whole thing quite exciting."

"I saw that," JB said. "It probably caused the biggest stink in British television history. No one, not anyone, had ever sworn on television before."

"Bill Grundy asked for it," Sandy said forcefully. "If he hadn't prompted them into saying something outrageous, all that swearing would probably never have happened."

"That's right, didn't one of the band call him a fucking rotter or something?" JB said as he sat back down.

Sandy nodded.

"I reckon it was Bill Grundy, the Today show and all that swearing that took punk rock mainstream," Sandy said.

The door opened and one punk after another entered the pub. Two carried guitars and another struggled with drums.

"Here, GBH," Sandy called.

The lead singer placed a snare drum on a table and turned to face her.

"What are Kleptos?" Sandy asked.

"Kleptos is short for Kleptomaniacs, you know, the irresistible urge to steal stuff and getting pleasure from what you've nicked."

"Oh, okay," Sandy replied.

Al watched the punks carry the instruments to the back of the pub before turning back to all of those at the table.

"I suppose that in some strange way that makes us all kleptomaniacs," Al said with chuckle.

Sandy turned to Brian and smiled.

"I fell in love a kleptomaniac... He stole my heart,"

"Have a word," Leaky said with a loud, dissonant laugh.

279

Al sniggered to himself as he witnessed Brian getting embarrassed.

"What did Brian the sociopath say to his kleptomaniac girlfriend...? I'm gonna steal your heart," Al thought as he chuckled into his beer glass.

"Has anybody heard any more about this mob from Leicester?" Al said, wiping the froth of beer from his mouth.

"I heard that two working girls were stabbed on the street," JB said matter-of-factly. "Nothing too serious."

"I was talking to a couple of guys from the Stores," Black Sandra said as she reached under the table and rubbed her hand up and down Al's thigh. "They reckon a couple of punters looking for girls had a few too many and were beaten up and robbed. They couldn't be sure, but it sounded like the Leicester mob."

The Scottish Stores pub was known by the locals as the 'Stores'.

"I thought after the kicking they got in here the other night they would have fucked off back up the M1 motorway," Leaky said.

"Not a chance," Al thought as he turned to watch the Teenage Kleptos set up. *"The Kings Cross prize is too big. It's not worth thousands...it's worth millions."*

"Do you reckon they'll be back?" Black Sandra said as she moved her hand from Al's thigh and clutched the loaded gun in her handbag.

"It's possible," Al said calmly. "If they create a problem in any of the Speelers, the pubs I protect, or hurt any of the girls on our patch, we'll hit them hard... fucking hard."

Sandra released the handgun.

After another two rounds of drinks, the tribe of anarchic punk fans began to flood the pub en-masse.

"I can't sit here and listen to that shit," JB said before swallowing the last of drink and rising to his feet. "I'll wait to hear from you, Leaky."

"Yeah, right," Leaky said.

"Be lucky," Black Sandra said, winking at Leaky.

As the door closed, Black Sandra ran her hand to the top of Al's thigh and whispered into his ear.

"Are you coming back to mine later tonight?"

"What time?"

"My girls have a show to do in Camden Town, so I'll be home around midnight," Black Sandra whispered before gently kissing his ear.

"I'll do my rounds and then come over," Al said with a flirtatious wink.

"Well I can't sit around here all day gassing with you lot," Black Sandra said before leaving the pub.

Leaky exaggeratedly sniffed his armpits.

"Is it me or does everyone actually have to leave?" Leaky said as he motioned the barman to pour another round of drinks.

"Well I've got to go too," Sandy said as she stood up. "But don't worry, I'll pick you up some deodorant while I'm out."

Al and Brian sniggered as Leaky feigned being hurt by Sandy's comments.

"Yeah, get him some Brut," Al said. "It'll make a nice change from the smell of cigarettes, booze and weird sex."

Brian almost choked on his pint.

"What do you mean weird sex?"

"Leaky, I think the world of you mate but there is something not quite right about carrying a selection of dildos around with you like mechanics do spanners," Al said with a snigger.

"I'm offended," Leaky said with a gaping smile.

"You'll get over it," Al said before thanking the barman for bringing the drinks to the table.

"Already have," Leaky said with a half-supressed laugh.

The pub was rapidly filling with the regulars, working girls, punters and punk rockers.

Al spotted Buddy at the bar with his two mates Josh and Riot. Buddy swivelled around and raised his glass.

"Harmless," Al thought as he watched the band getting ready to start.

"Yeah right," GBH bellowed out from the stage. "I'm GBH and we are... Teenage Kleptos!"

The colourful, anarchic, punk audience yelled out and clapped their hands.

GBH guzzled down the last of his pint before grabbing his microphone.

'One... Two...Three... Four!"

The guitarist and drummer pounded their instruments, producing a short, fast paced rhythm while GBH yelled out a melody of hard edged, anti-establishment, songs. At first the punk audience rocked back and forth slowly. A few of the punks began to pogo on the spot while furiously shaking their heads.

"This is shit," Leaky said, turning his nose up.

"It's not everyone's cup of tea," Al said, watching the band and the pogoing audience. "But it sells beer."

"Those punk girls really are something else," Al thought as a young girl with half her hair dyed black and the other half a bright red leapt up and down in her high leg, ox-blood coloured, Doctor Marten Boots.

Al continued to watch the punk as her pleated tartan skirt rose up and down. She wore a black leather bomber style jacket with three large stainless-steel chains sewn across the back and a chain with a padlock around her neck.

"Something incredibly sexy about that punk rocker look for sure," Al thought.

GBH jumped around the make-shift stage and began to bellow the band's signature tune.

'Teenage Kleptos rule

It's cool when we bunk school

Red hair and tattoos

Dog collars and Doc Marten Boots!'

The pogoing became increasingly aggressive as the punks expressed their enjoyment. They pushed one another, knocking over other customer's drinks, and slammed into each other with one young punk with short raven black spikey hair rolling over a full table and landing on the floor.

'Teenage Kleptos.... We're so mean

Teenage Kleptos... We'll smash your teeth

Teenage Kleptos... We're so fucking tough

Teenage Kleptos... We're so rough!'

The punk rockers began to spit at each other, at the band and gobbed at the pub's customers while becoming increasingly energetic.

'Let's get rowdy… Let's get drunk

We are Teenage Kleptos… We are punk!'

Al could see that the customers were not happy as beer and glasses fell or were pushed off the tables. He sprang to his feet, scanned the pogoing punks for Buddy with the green Mohican hair.

"Got yer!" Al said to himself as he bounded across the bar.

"Oi, Buddy," Al said as he tapped him hard on the shoulder. "You need to get a grip of yourself and this lot!"

"What?" Buddy yelled out as he turned but continued to pogo up and down on the spot.

"All this gobbing and smashing things up is out of order," Al said firmly. "Now get a fucking grip!"

With his eyes wide open and still jumping manically around, Buddy hocked up a horrendous phlegm and gobbed it straight into Al's face.

No sooner had the spit hit Al than he hurled a devastating right hook followed by a rapid fierce uppercut that put Buddy flat on his back. From the corner of his eye, he saw Riot, Buddy's friend, charging towards him like a savage lion. Al shifted his feet and launched a calamitous combination of left and right hooks followed by a rapid succession of jabs and a final uppercut that had Riot spark out on the carpet. Brian steamed across the pub with fists and boots flying as the punk rockers knocked over tables, attacked and gobbed at customers. On stage GBH grabbed the guitar from the lead guitarist and leapt off the stage with the electric guitar held high above his head.

Brian grabbed one young punk rocker by the shirt collar and brought his forehead down on the punk rocker's nose with such ferocity that it shattered. Brian threw him to one side like a discarded action man toy just as GBH landed and swung the instrument over his head. Brian side stepped the attack. The guitar smashed onto the carpet and broke into several pieces held together only by the strings. GBH was wide open for attack. Brian reached out and grabbed the lead singer by his bright red hair and yanked it down with tremendous force onto his rising knee.

CRACK!

GBH's legs crumpled beneath him.

The remaining punk rockers knocked over tables and chairs as they scattered across the bar to the exit

Al was scanning the escaping punk rockers for Buddy and Riot's friend Josh.

Within just seconds the Bell was cleared of all the punk rockers. Al's eyes landed on two punk rocker girls standing by the bar with their hands held up high, indicating that they had nothing to do with the trouble. He recognised the girl with the red and black hair as the one he had been drooling over earlier. She held his gaze for two, maybe three seconds before offering a smile and mouthing 'Bye'.

The two girls left the pub to join their punk rocker friends outside. Leaky, Brian and Al helped Buddy, GBH and Riot to their feet before helping them to the door.

"Buddy, don't come here again," Al said as he gave him one final shove out onto the pavement.

"I told you I didn't like the look of them," Leaky said as he handed Al a pint.

"Just spirited youngsters looking for some kind of purpose and direction in this crazy, fucked up, world," Al thought as took a long sip from his glass.

Chapter 30

It had been a late night at the American Bar and after locking up, just after 4.00am, Al stayed over at Black Sandra's squat. He was awake early and decided to leave Black Sandra in bed to take a walk around Kings Cross and the surrounding area. It struck him that breakfast at George's Café on the York Way near the junction of Wharfdale Road would nice. Al inhaled the mid-morning London air before stopping to gaze up at the Great Northern Hotel on Pancras Road. It was one of the country's earliest purpose-built railway hotels. He continued down to the West Handyside Canopy in Wharf Road and continued to The Midland Grand Hotel. Al peered up at the gothic masterpiece.

"It doesn't matter how many times I stroll around Kings Cross I'll never take this wonderful place for granted," Al thought before his attention was taken by three red buses. *"Typical. Late, and when they do arrive it's in threes."*

Al found himself reflecting on his time back in London since his release from HMP Pentonville.

"I've done alright," Al thought as he smiled to himself. *"From the new kid on the block I'm now protecting fifteen pubs, legally. Taking a cut on all the villainy within the pubs and have two Speelers that are packed seven days a week with everyone having a great time and making money. Life is good…. Damn good!"*

Al pushed both his hands into his trouser pockets as he passed by London's shoppers and the tourists flocking in and out of the shops.

"My no strings thing with Black Sandra works well and true to her word, she doesn't flinch or even raise an eyebrow when I take a fancy to something else," Al thought as his upper lip curled into a broad smile. *"My brother Brian and Sandy are here which has been great. We may not always see eye to eye on everything but he's a*

good brother and I can't think of anyone I'd rather have backing me up when there's trouble. Wullie... I haven't forgiven that bastard yet for what he did to my dog."

Al stopped outside George's Café and read the breakfast specials that had been handwritten with felt tip pens onto lime green star shaped cards. He settled on eggs, bacon, sausage and beans with a round of toast.

"I could have gone back to smash and grabs on jewellers or even taken up armed robberies," Al thought as he remembered counting up a little over ten thousand pounds from his last week's takings. *"But there are smarter ways to make money and there is still more I can do."*

"Thanks George," Al called out as he put his knife and fork together on the breakfast plate.

As he walked back towards Caledonian Road, he checked his watch.

"Breakfast... it's closer to dinner time," Al thought. *"I'll pop into the Bell for a swift couple before meeting Limerick Mick down at Manny's Amusement Arcade later."*

Al pushed open the door to the Bell pub and stepped inside. He felt an overwhelming surge of happiness wash over him as he scanned the pub before resting his gaze on his regular table where Black Sandra and Leaky were sitting. Leaky had his black sports bag on the table filled to the brim with forged five-pound notes. Al watched as he took payment before handing over a huge wad on notes.

"Business is good all around," Al thought before attracting the barman's attention, ordering a round, and joining his friends.

Just as Al sat down, the door opened, and two young punk rocker girls stepped inside and stopped by his table.

"Fuck me!" Al thought as he recognised the punk girl with the wild red and jet-black hair. She wore a dog chain around her neck and a

black leather top brought together with adjustable buckles over her pert young breasts. Her matching leather mini skirt had side adjustable buckles leading down to black fish net tights and black ten-hole Doctor Marten Boots.

Al could feel his mouth go dry as his gaze strayed to her friend in the black PVC dominatrix peaked cap with decorative silver trim. The punk wore a black t-shirt, fashionably ripped, with oversized safety pins and the words 'No Fun' painted on in red. His eyes moved down to her tight black shorts, ripped black tights and Doctor Marten Boots.

Al couldn't help but notice that Black Sandra's mouth had fallen open.

"These girls are walking sex," Al thought.

"You're Al," the punk with the red and black hair said. "I'm Debs and this is my friend Felicity... we all call her Fliss."

"Yeah, I'm Al."

"We just wanted you to know that we had nothing to do with that trouble last week," Debs said as she held Al's gaze.

"That was nothing," Al said. "It was quickly sorted out."

"So, is it alright if Fliss and I still come in here?" Debs said as she fluttered her eyelids.

"You're both very welcome to come in here anytime you like," Black Sandra said. "Isn't that right, Al?"

Al nodded.

"Join us," Al said as he motioned for them to sit down.

"Drink, girls?" Black Sandra said as she raised her hand to attract the barman's attention.

"Lager, please," Debs said.

"I'll have a lager too," Fliss said as she reached into her bag and produced a pack of Rothman cigarettes.

"Cigarette?" Fliss said as she offered the pack around.

Only Black Sandra took a cigarette. Al watched as Black Sandra leaned right in to the lighter's flame.

"I think she fancies these girls," Al thought as he watched Black Sandra reach out and stroke the girl's shoulder once her cigarette was lit.

"So where do you girls come from?" Al said as he reached for his pint.

"Sutton, we came up on the Northern Line from Morden," Debs said. "We met Buddy, Riot and Josh on the Kings Road after a night out and he was telling everyone about this place and how he had a gig all lined up. My friend, Matty said that he knew of them, and we should give it a miss, but with Teenage Kleptos confirming the gig, we came anyway."

"What, are they supposed to be troublemakers?" Leaky said.

Debs chuckled and shook her head.

"No, no," she said with a broad smile. "Buddy, Riot and Josh come from Richmond and are what we would call 'wannabe's'. You might know the type, public school, middle class and pockets full of daddy's money. They're just trying to shock their parents and make a name for themselves."

"Like I thought at the time...harmless," Al thought.

"Buddy, Riot and GBH all had to go hospital," Debs said as she scrunched up her nose. "Riot's face is a bit of a mess, but he'll get over it. GBH and Buddy will embellish the facts to friends and live off it for the next twelve months."

"No real harm done," Al said as he held Debs' eye contact.

Debs shook her head.

"I'm curious," Black Sandra said as she raised her drink to her lips. "Do you girls have boyfriends… or girlfriends?"

The two punks looked at each and giggled.

In the background *'Whatever You Want'* by Status Quo was playing on the jukebox.

"Neither of us do the whole serious relationship thing," Debs said.

"We don't want to be owned or to have some kind of a hold on someone else," Fliss said as she reached for her lager.

"Was it a bad experience?" Black Sandra said as she ogled at Fliss over her drink.

"There was one boy that I thought was kind of special at the beginning, but it quickly turned toxic. He would want to tell me what to wear, where I could and couldn't go and finally, he tried to break up our friendship out of jealousy," Fliss said as she leaned back into her chair.

"Toxic relationships take time to heal and for the emotions to fully recover," Black Sandra said. "You did extremely well to recognise the relationship for what it was and call an end to it, well done!"

"Thank you," Fliss said, blushing.

"What about you, Debs?" Al said as he swivelled in his chair to face her.

"I am in no rush to find some kind of a long-term relationship with a boy or a girl. I'm fiercely independent and thoroughly enjoy casual dates, hanging out with friends at pubs, clubs on the Kings Road and being single. Besides, I'm still discovering who I am and my life choices. One thing is for certain, that is that anything long term would need to be built on a firm foundation of friendship."

"It sounds like you've well and truly thought it through," Al said.

Debs smiled.

"What about you Al?"

"I can answer that for you Al," Black Sandra said.

"Fine, okay" Al said as he leaned back and let Black Sandra take the lead.

"Al and I are friends, very good friends," Black Sandra said as she alternated her gaze from Debs to Fliss. We occasionally share the same bed but have no commitment to each other. We both see other people without fear or jealousy and that works extremely well for us."

"How incredibly grown up and liberated," Debs said before inhaling deeply. "I'm impressed and pleased for you both."

"Don't kill this Black Sandra," Al thought. *"I could be in here."*

"I like both men and woman," Black Sandra said in a soft, sultry tone. "I'm attracted to the person, not their genitalia."

"I'm straight," Al said with a hint of awkwardness.

"Have you ever kissed a girl?" Black Sandra said as she turned back to Fliss with a prolonged, intense, eye contact.

Fliss smiled awkwardly before running her hand through her jet-black spikey hair.

"Did you enjoy it?"

Fliss immediately turned to Debs and then back to Black Sandra.

"It was a very nice, special, experience," Fliss said gracefully.

"I had my first girl on girl liaison with my best friend," Black Sandra said as she closed her eyes. "I'll never forget it, or her."

"Where is this going?" Al thought. *"We could both be in here."*

"Can we get you all a drink?" Debs said as she opened her small black star-studded purse.

Al looked down at his watch.

"I can't right now as I have to meet someone about a bit of business," Al said as he rose from his chair. "I'll only be gone about an hour or so. Will you still be here?"

"We're having a good time," Debs said as she twirled her hair. "We're not going anywhere."

"Al, I'll walk with you," Black Sandra said before swallowing the last few drops in her glass.

With *'Up the Junction'* by Squeeze playing in the background, Al motioned for the barman to bring over two more pints of lager for Debs and Fliss and a whiskey for Leaky.

"Nice girls," Al said as they stepped out onto Caledonian Road.

"Two extremely nice girls," Black Sandra said as she reached into her handbag and took out a small bag of cocaine. "They're casual, fun, light-hearted and warm."

"Am I sensing that you fancy one or both of them?" Al said with a wry grin.

Black Sandra stopped to snort the line of cocaine from the side of her hand.

"Hmmm," Black Sandra muttered as the invigorating sense of intense euphoria surged through her body.

"They're open, honest, relaxed, confident and sexy. I'd like to fuck them both... and you at the same time," Black Sandra whispered in a low, erotic tone.

"Fucking hell!" Al thought as he felt his manhood swell rapidly and press tightly against his trousers. *"Oh yes... yes, please! Make that happen!"*

"When this business of yours is done we'll go back to the Bell, have a few more drinks and then invite them back to my place to see how far this will go," Black Sandra said as the cocaine kicked in the increased level of self-confidence.

Manny's Amusement Arcade was packed with brightly lit pinball machines, claw cranes, slot machines and a long line of coin operated games. *'On My Radio'* by The Selector pounded out of the speaker system.

"Al, over here."

Al looked over to see Limerick Mick standing by five brand new 'Space Invader' machines.

"Hello mate," Al said as he shook Limerick Mick's hand warmly. "This is Black Sandra."

"Hello darling."

Limerick Mick pointed at the new machines. "See these... Space Invaders... this is the future of arcades like this."

"I've never played," Al said.

"I've heard that arcades up and down the country have been full of kids and adults playing these for hours on end," Limerick Mick said as he patted the machine.

"I wanted to talk to you about a bit of security," Limerick Mick said before veering to look over Al's right shoulder. "Who the fuck are they?"

Al turned swiftly on his heels to see eight of the Leicester mob steaming towards him with gritted teeth, clenched fists and pickaxe handles.

Instinctively Al ran forward and with one almighty heave turned the coin operated pool table over on its side.

"Run!" Al yelled out to Black Sandra.

Al managed to duck out of the way from the first swing of a pickaxe handle. With adrenaline racing through his body, he jumped back up onto his feet and fired a rapid succession of left and right punches.

CRACK!

Al felt a sharp pain to the side of his face as the Leicester lad pulled back the pickaxe handle ready to swing again.

SMACK!

SMACK!

CRACK!

CRUNCH!

Al soaked up the kicks and punches and tried desperately to defend himself, but the violence was relentless.

SMACK!

CRACK!

THUD!

Al could feel his legs giving way as kick after kick connected.

"I'm losing, I'm fucking losing," Al thought as the hoard of angry boots battered his body.

Al's legs collapsed from under him. His face and body suffered punch after punch.

"I can't punch... I'm going down" Al thought as his body lay on the cold tile floor.

With *'The Tide is High'* by Blondie booming out of the speakers, Black Sandra screamed at the top of her voice for the mob to stop, while frantically rummaging through her handbag.

"This is it… the end… I'm going to die," Al thought as two Leicester lads whacked, hammered and pummelled his limp body with their pickaxe handles.

"Leave him alone!" Black Sandra shouted as she gripped her Beretta handgun tightly.

The Leicester Mob continued their merciless, unabated vicious attack on Al.

Black Sandra dropped her handbag and held the gun in both hands.

"Stop… You're killing him!"

Books by Al McIntosh

With Dean Rinaldi

Villain No Remorse

Villain No Remorse II

Villain No Remorse III

Villain No Remorse IV

Contact:

Facebook: Al McIntosh Author

Facebook: Georgian, Victorian and Edwardian Crime

Facebook: Dean Rinaldi Ghostwriter Publisher Mentor. www.deanrinaldi-ghostwriter.com

Printed in Great Britain
by Amazon

85561107R00169